GUIDE TO NUMERICAL ANALYSIS

Consultant Editor: David A. Towers,
Senior Lecturer in Mathematics,
University of Lancaster

The Titles in this Series:

Abstract Algebra
Linear Algebra
Numerical Analysis

Further titles are in preparation.

Guide to Numerical Analysis

Peter R. Turner

Department of Mathematics
University of Lancaster
Lancaster, UK

and

Mathematics Department
United States Naval Academy
Annapolis, MD 21402, USA

MACMILLAN

First published 1989

Published by
MACMILLAN EDUCATION LTD
Houndmills, Basingstoke, Hampshire RG21 2XS
and London
Companies and representatives
throughout the world

Printed in Hong Kong

British Library Cataloguing in Publication Data
Turner, Peter
Guide to numerical analysis
1. Numerical analysis. Computation
I. Title
519.4
ISBN 0–333–44947–9

To my wife, Pat, for her
patience and encouragement throughout

CONTENTS

EDITOR'S FOREWORD

Wide concern has been expressed in tertiary education about the difficulties experienced by students during their first year of an undergraduate course containing a substantial component of mathematics. These difficulties have a number of underlying causes, including the change of emphasis from an algorithmic approach at school to a more rigorous and abstract approach in undergraduate studies, the greater expectation of independent study, and the increased pace at which material is presented. The books in this series are intended to be sensitive to these problems.

Each book is a carefully selected, short, introductory text on a key area of the first-year syllabus; the areas are complementary and largely self-contained. Throughout, the pace of development is gentle, sympathetic and carefully motivated. Clear and detailed explanations are provided, and important concepts and results are stressed.

As mathematics is a practical subject which is best learned by doing it, rather than watching or reading about someone else doing it, a particular effort has been made to include a plentiful supply of worked examples, together with appropriate exercises, ranging in difficulty from the straightforward to the challenging.

When one goes fellwalking, the most breathtaking views require some expenditure of effort in order to gain access to them: nevertheless, the peak is more likely to be reached if a gentle and interesting route is chosen. The mathematical peaks attainable in these books are every bit as exhilarating, the paths are as gentle as we could find, and the interest and expectation are maintained throughout to prevent the spirits from flagging on the journey.

Lancaster, 1989

David A. Towers
Consultant Editor

PREFACE

This book has been developed from course notes for a variety of introductory courses in numerical methods and analysis which I have taught at the University of Lancaster and the University of Maryland. The level and content of these courses have varied considerably but have included all the material covered here. The intention of this book is to provide a gentle and sympathetic introduction to many of the basic problems of scientific computing and the wide variety of methods used for their solution. The book is therefore suitable as a first course in numerical mathematics or computation for first-year undergraduates—whether they are intending mathematicians or users of mathematics such as engineers, scientists or economists.

This, of course, precludes the possibility of providing a fully rigorous treatment of all the most up-to-date algorithms and their analyses. The intention is rather to give an appreciation of the need for numerical methods for the solution of different types of problem and to discuss the basic approaches. For each of the problems, this is followed by at least some mathematical justification and, most importantly, examples to provide both practical justification of the methods and motivation for the reader. The level of mathematical justification is determined largely by the desire to keep the assumed prerequisite mathematical knowledge to a minimum. Thus, for example, no knowledge of linear algebra is assumed beyond the most basic matrix algebra and analytic results are based only on a sound knowledge of A-level calculus and the ability to *apply* the intermediate-value theorem and mean-value theorem. Inevitably this means that some methods such as those for the numerical solution of differential equations are not derived in a detailed and rigorous manner. Such methods are nonetheless justified and/or derived by appealing to other techniques discussed earlier in the book such as those for numerical integration and differentiation. In contrast, in situations where rigorous explanation can be included without creating bafflement rather than enlightenment, this is given. In the chapter on iterative solution of equations, for instance, the introductory sections are followed by a brief formal treatment of convergence of sequences and then a discussion of the convergence of iterative schemes. The formal treatment of convergence of sequences and the later section on convergence of series could easily be omitted from a first course in numerical methods for engineering students.

The practical justification is provided by examples and exercises many of which make use of the BASIC programs which are included for several methods. The provision of such practical 'justification' necessitates the careful, even if empirical, consideration of errors and their control. Chapter 1 is devoted to floating-point arithmetic and errors and, throughout the subsequent chapters, we take time to consider the precision of our numerical solutions and how this can be safeguarded or improved.

The use of BASIC as a programming language is intended to make the book more easily accessible to students who have no background in computing. Many of the exercises will demand only minor changes to the given programs while very few require the writing of a program from scratch. BASIC serves this purpose well as it is both a highly 'readable' language— especially in the fairly powerful form used here—and it is a good preparation for more advanced programming in a high-level language such as FORTRAN. It should therefore be possible for a student with virtually no prior knowledge of computing to be able to understand what is going on in the programs and to make intelligent use of them to enhance his or her understanding of the methods under discussion. The programs are not intended to be sophisticated or robust pieces of software but are simply illustrative.

The intention of the book as a whole is to provide the student with an introduction to this subject which is not in its combined demands of computing, motivation, manipulation and analysis paced such that only the most able can 'see the wood for the trees'. The major effort of programming is thus removed from the reader as are the harder parts of the analysis. The algebraic manipulation is largely unavoidable but is carefully explained— especially in the early stages. The motivation for the numerical methods is provided by the examples—which are not all of types which can be solved directly—and the numerical methods themselves provide motivation for the necessary analysis.

Finally, I must thank two close friends for their help in getting this book 'off the ground'. David Towers, as editor of the series, has been a willing adviser and a great encouragement. Charles Clenshaw has been of invaluable help in reading the draft versions of each of the chapters and suggesting many improvements in style, presentation and mathematics.

Lancaster, 1988   Peter R. Turner

1 NUMBER REPRESENTATIONS AND ERRORS

1.1 INTRODUCTION

In this book, we shall consider some of the fundamental ideas of mathematical and, in particular, numerical computing. These in turn form the basis of most of the techniques of scientific computing which are widely used in almost every branch of scientific work and in business and economic applications.

However, we do not deal here solely with the methodology of solving these problems on a computer. We shall also consider in some detail the important underlying mathematical ideas—the reasons why our methods work (or do not work!). This course therefore serves not just as an introduction to this area of applicable mathematics, **numerical analysis**, but also to the ideas of mathematical analysis.

After a brief look at the ways in which numbers are stored and manipulated in computers and the errors which result from this representation and arithmetic, we shall be concerned with fundamental mathematical problems such as the solution of equations, the evaluation of functions and their integrals, and the solution of differential equations. Your school experience may suggest that these are not really problems at all but, as we shall see in these various contexts, the range of problems which can be solved *exactly* is very limited indeed. We therefore require efficient methods of obtaining good *approximate* solutions and (and this is one of the major aspects of numerical analysis) the ability to estimate how good, or bad, our approximations are.

Before proceeding to any of the specific topics of this introductory chapter, it is worth pointing out that we shall be introducing several definitions and concepts which will be unfamiliar. The reader should not spend time trying to master all these immediately but should rather try to acquire a rough idea of the sorts of difficulties which can arise from the computer solution of mathematical problems.

1.2 FLOATING-POINT NUMBERS

Within any electronic computer, since the machine itself is finite, we can represent only a finite set of numbers, but of course the set of real numbers which we use in, for example, calculus is infinite. It is therefore necessary to decide on an efficient method of representing numbers in a computer so that we reach an acceptable compromise between the **range** of numbers available to us and the **accuracy** or **precision** of their representation. The way this is usually achieved is to use the **floating-point number** system which is, in principle, much like the scientific notation used for many physical constants and in the display of hand-calculators.

Example 1.2.1

The number π would be represented in the (normalised) decimal system using four significant **digits** by

$$\pi \approx 0.3142 \times 10^1$$

or with six significant digits by

$$\pi \approx 0.314\,159 \times 10^1.$$

In the binary system working to 18 significant figures, or **bits**, we have

$$\pi \approx 0.110010010000111111 \times 2^2.$$

Here the digits following the *binary* point represent increasing powers of $\frac{1}{2}$ so that the first five of these *bits* represent

$$\frac{1}{2} + \frac{1}{4} + \frac{0}{8} + \frac{0}{16} + \frac{1}{32}.$$

The other popular base for computer number systems is 16, the **hexadecimal** or **hex** system. Each hexadecimal digit is a whole number between 0 and 15 and can be expressed in binary form using 4 bits. The standard notation for extending the decimal system to base 16 is to write A, B, C, D, E and F to denote 10, 11, 12, 13, 14 and 15. The above binary representation could thus be written as

$$\pi \approx 0.0011\,0010\,0100\,0011\,1111 \times 2^4,$$

and so we see that the hexadecimal representation using five hexadecimal places is

$$\pi \approx 0.3243F \times 16^1,$$

where the fraction consists of hexadecimal digits and F is the hexadecimal 'digit' for 15. Each hexadecimal digit in this expression is obtained by reading off the next four binary figures. The change in the binary exponent was chosen simply to obtain a power of $16 = 2^4$. The whole expression thus denotes

$$\left(\frac{3}{16} + \frac{2}{16^2} + \frac{4}{16^3} + \frac{3}{16^4} + \frac{15}{16^5} \right) \times 16 \approx 3.141\,586,$$

which has error no more than, or *bounded by*, a half in the final (hexadecimal) place. That is, the error is bounded by $\frac{1}{2} \times 16 \times 16^{-5} \approx 0.000\,008$.

In general, a positive number x can be expressed in terms of an arbitrary base β as

$$x = (a_n a_{n-1} \ldots a_1 a_0, b_1 b_2 \ldots b_m)_\beta,$$

which represents the quantity

$$a_n \beta^n + a_{n-1} \beta^{n-1} + \ldots + a_1 \beta + a_0 + b_1 \beta^{-1} + b_2 \beta^{-2} + \ldots + b_m \beta^m,$$

and each of the base-β digits $a_n, \ldots, a_0, b_1, \ldots, b_m$ is an integer in the range $0, 1, 2, \ldots, \beta - 1$. Such a number may be expressed in floating-point form as

$$x = f \beta^E, \tag{1.1}$$

where the **fraction** or **mantissa** f satisfies

$$\beta^{-1} \leqslant f < 1 \tag{1.2}$$

and the **exponent** E is an integer.

This is the basis of the **normalised** floating-point system used in almost every computer. (An unnormalised system need not satisfy equation (1.2).) Equation (1.1) is replaced by an approximate equation in which the mantissa f is represented to a fixed number of significant (base-β) figures.

In the above example, the implicit assumption has been made that the representation uses **symmetric rounding** and so a number is represented by the nearest member of the set of machine numbers. This is by no means the universal **abbreviation rule** adopted by computer systems; one common alternative is to use **chopping** in which any positive number would be represented by the largest machine number which does not exceed it. Thus, for example, π would be represented as $0.314\,16 \times 10^1$ to five significant digits if symmetric rounding were used but as $0.314\,15 \times 10^1$ with chopping. Most of what follows will not be affected by the specific abbreviation rule used and so, unless stated otherwise, we shall assume that symmetric rounding is used.

It should be noted here that most computer systems and programming languages allow quantities which are known to be integers to be represented in their exact binary form. This of course restricts the size of integers which can be represented in a single computer **word** (that is, some fixed number of characters) but does avoid the introduction of any additional errors as a result of the representation. The errors in the representation of real numbers, however, also affect the accuracy of any subsequent calculations using them. We shall be considering this in some detail in the next few sections but, for now, we illustrate some of the possible effects with a few examples.

Examples 1.2.2

Consider the following simple operations on a hypothetical decimal computer in which the result of every arithmetic operation is rounded to four significant digits.

1
$$0.1234 \times 10^1 + 0.1234 \times 10^0 = 0.135\,74 \times 10^1$$
$$\approx 0.1357 \times 10^1$$

has a **rounding error** of 4×10^{-4} which is also true of the corresponding subtraction

$$0.1234 \times 10^1 - 0.1234 \times 10^0 = 0.111\,06 \times 10^1$$
$$\approx 0.1111 \times 10^1.$$

The multiplication of the same pair of numbers yields the exact result $0.152\,275\,6$ which would be represented on our machine as 0.1523×10^0 and so is also subject to a small rounding error.

2 The somewhat more complicated piece of arithmetic

$$\frac{1.234}{0.1234} - \frac{1.234}{0.1233}$$

demonstrates some of the pitfalls rather more dramatically. Proceeding in the order suggested by the layout of the formula, we obtain

$$\frac{1.234}{0.1234} \approx 0.1000 \times 10^2$$

and

$$\frac{1.234}{0.1233} \approx 0.1001 \times 10^2,$$

and hence the result -0.0001×10^2 which on normalisation becomes -0.1000×10^{-1}.

If, however, we proceed rather differently and compute first

$$\frac{1}{0.1234} - \frac{1}{0.1233} \approx 8.104 - 8.110$$

$$\approx -0.6000 \times 10^{-2}$$

and then multiply this result by 1.234, we get -0.7404×10^{-2}, a considerably more accurate approximation to the correct result which to the same precision is -0.8110×10^{-2}.

The examples above illustrate some basic truths about computer arithmetic and rounding errors but again it is worth emphasising that you should not be perturbed if all the details are not immediately clear. Firstly, we see that, because the number representation used is not exact, the introduction of further error as a result of arithmetic is inevitable. In particular, the subtraction of two numbers of similar magnitudes results invariably in the loss of some precision. (The result of our first approach has only one significant figure since the zeros introduced after the normalisation are entirely spurious.) There is in general nothing that can be done to avoid this phenomenon but, as the second approach to the calculation demonstrates, we can alleviate matters by taking care over the order in which a piece of computation takes place.

There are two other related problems which can result from the finiteness of the set of machine numbers. Suppose that on the same hypothetical machine as we used in Examples 1.2.2 there is one decimal digit allocated to the exponent of a floating-point number. Then, since

$$0.3456 \times 10^4 \times 0.3456 \times 10^8 = 3456 \times 34\,560\,000$$

$$= 119\,439\,360\,000$$

$$\approx 0.1194 \times 10^{12},$$

the result of this operation is too large to be represented in our hypothetical machine. Such an event is called **overflow**. Similarly, if the result of an arithmetic operation is too small to be represented, then it is termed **underflow**. In the case of our example this would occur if the exponent of the normalised result were less than -9.

Fortunately, such catastrophic situations quite rarely result from correct computation but even some apparently straightforward tasks must be programmed very carefully in order to avoid overflow or underflow since their occurrence will cause a program to fail.

We have already pointed out that the floating-point representation is not the only one used in computers since integers can be stored exactly, or in the **fixed-point number** form. For several years in the infancy of the computer, this was the only number representation available and calculations needed to be scaled so as to avoid overflow and underflow. Today, a similar deficiency is becoming evident in the floating-point system and new number representations have been proposed in order to try to avoid overflow and underflow altogether.

1.3 SOURCES OF ERRORS

Of course the most common source of error in any mathematical process is just human blunder but for the purpose of this discussion we shall assume infallibility of both the mathematician and the computer programmer. Even in this fantasy world, errors are an everyday fact of computational life. The full analysis of these errors—their sources, interactions and combined effect—and the right strategy to minimise their effect on a complicated computational process can be a very difficult task and is certainly way beyond the scope of this book.

In this section, we consider just three of the principal sources of error. In several places, we shall cite examples of methods which may well be unfamiliar at this stage. These are purely illustrative and you should not be too concerned about following the details.

Rounding errors

As we have already seen these arise from the storage of numbers to a fixed number of binary or decimal places or significant figures.

Example 1.3.1

The equation

$$x^2 - 10.1x + 1 = 0$$

has the exact solutions 10 and 0.1 but, if the quadratic formula is used on a hypothetical four-decimal digit machine, the roots obtained are 10.00 and 0.1005; the errors being due to the rounding of all numbers involved in the calculation to four significant figures.

If however, we use this same formulae for the larger root together with the fact that the product of the roots is 1, then of course we obtain the values 10.00 and 0.1000. Thus, we see that the effect of the rounding error can be reduced (in this case eliminated) by the careful choice of numerical process or the **design of the algorithm**. (It is worth remarking that a quadratic equation with real roots should *always* be solved this way.)

Note that this is based on symmetric rounding; if the abbreviation were done using chopping, then the value 9.995 would have been obtained for the larger root.

Truncation error

This is the name given to the errors which result from the many ways in which a numerical process can be cut short or truncated. Obvious examples are the use of a finite number of terms of a series to estimate its sum—for example, in routines for evaluating elementary functions or numerical methods for solving differential equations (see chapters 3–6). With insufficient care, such errors can lead us back to blunders since, for example, working to any specified accuracy, the **harmonic series**

$$1 + \frac{1}{2} + \frac{1}{3} + \ldots = \sum_{n=1}^{\infty} \frac{1}{n}$$

appears to converge. If we work to two decimal places with correct rounding, then each term beyond $n = 200$ will be treated as zero and so we might conclude that, to two decimal places,

$$\sum_{n=1}^{\infty} \frac{1}{n} \approx \sum_{n=1}^{200} \frac{1}{n}$$

$$\approx 6.16,$$

but we shall see later that this sum is, in fact, *infinite*!

The difficulty here is caused partly by truncation and partly by rounding error. In order to claim that some finite number of terms gives the sum of an infinite series to a specified accuracy, we must ensure that all the remaining terms in the series do not affect the sum to that accuracy. (It would also be necessary for such a routine to work to a higher accuracy than is required in the final result.)

Example 1.3.2

Determine the number of terms of the exponential series required to estimate e to three decimal places.

We consider here just the truncation error by assuming that the calculations are performed exactly. Now

$$e = \exp 1 = 1 + 1 + \frac{1}{2!} + \frac{1}{3!} + \ldots$$

$$= \sum_{n=0}^{\infty} \frac{1}{n!}.$$

The tail of this series can easily be bounded for any positive integer N by a geometric series as follows:

$$\sum_{n=N}^{\infty} \frac{1}{n!} = \frac{1}{N!} + \frac{1}{(N+1)!} + \ldots$$

$$\leqslant \left(1 + \frac{1}{N} + \frac{1}{N^2} + \ldots\right) \bigg/ N!$$

$$= \frac{1}{(N-1)(N-1)!},$$

7

and $1/(5 \times 5!) \approx 0.0017$ while $1/(6 \times 6!) \approx 0.0002$. Hence

$$2.7181 = \sum_{n=1}^{6} \frac{1}{n!}$$

$$\leqslant e$$

$$= \sum_{n=1}^{6} \frac{1}{n!} + \sum_{n=7}^{\infty} \frac{1}{n!}$$

$$\leqslant 2.7181 + 0.0002,$$

from which bounds we may conclude that $e = 2.718$ to three decimal places and that the first seven terms (that is those up to $1/6!$) are sufficient to yield this accuracy. Obviously, this calculation is also subject to rounding errors but in this case the accumulated rounding error has been kept under control by performing the calculation to much greater accuracy than was required in the result.

The errors in approximating a function by the first N terms of a Taylor series or in approximating an integral by Simpson's rule are examples of truncation error as is the error incurred by stopping an iteration when say two iterates agree to a certain number of decimal places.

Modelling errors and ill-conditioning

Frequently, in the mathematical modelling of physical or economic situations, simplifying assumptions are made which inevitably result in output errors. Such assumptions must of course be analysed to estimate their effect on the results. Sometimes this might be achieved by, for example, perturbing the value of some assumed constant and measuring the consequent change in the results.

If the model and the numerical method are stable, then small perturbations of input should result in small changes in the output. This is very closely related to the notion of conditioning. We illustrate the idea of an *ill-conditioned* problem with the classical example due to Wilkinson of finding the roots of the polynomial equation

$$p(x) = (x - 1)(x - 2)\dots(x - 20) = 0,$$

where p is given in the form

$$p(x) = x^{20} + a_{19}x^{19} + \dots + a_1 x + a_0.$$

If the coefficient $a_{19} = -210$ is changed by about 2^{-22}, then the resulting polynomial has only 10 real zeros and five complex conjugate pairs; and one of the real zeros is now at $x = 20.847$. A change of only one part in about 2 billion has certainly had significant effect!

Very rarely does a physical situation have such extreme inherent instability and so, if such ill-conditioning occurs in practice, the fault probably lies in the mathematical model and/or the data or in the mathematical techniques being used. All these should therefore be re-examined.

1.4 MEASURES OF ERROR AND PRECISION

The two most common error measures are the absolute and relative error in approximating a number x by a nearby number $\hat{x}$.

The **absolute error** is defined to be $|x - \hat{x}|$; this corresponds to the idea that x and $\hat{x}$ agree to a number of decimal places.

The **relative error** is usually defined to be $|x - \hat{x}|/|x| = |1 - \hat{x}/x|$ and corresponds to agreement to a number of significant figures. Because very often in a particular computation we do not have the true value x available, it is common to replace the x in the denominator of this definition by the approximation $\hat{x}$ in which case this error is given by $|1 - x/\hat{x}|$. (The asymmetric nature of this measure is somewhat unsatisfactory but this can be overcome by the alternative notion of relative precision.)

As a general principle, we expect absolute error to be more appropriate for numbers close to unity, while relative error seems more natural for large numbers or those close to zero. However, we must be wary—a relative error of 1% in a Moon shot could be sufficient to miss the Moon altogether!

For approximations to functions (as opposed to their values at particular points), other measures are used. These **metrics** are usually expressed in the form of measures of absolute error but are readily adapted for the purposes of relative error. The three most commonly used are defined for approximating a function f on an interval $[a, b]$ by another function or polynomial p: the **supremum** or L_∞ **metric**

$$\|f - p\|_\infty = \max_{a \leqslant x \leqslant b} |f(x) - p(x)|,$$

the L_1 **metric**

$$\|f - p\|_1 = \int_a^b |f(x) - p(x)| \, \mathrm{d}x$$

and the L_2 **metric**

$$\|f - p\|_2 = \left(\int_a^b |f(x) - p(x)|^2 \, \mathrm{d}x \right)^{1/2}$$

These **metrics** or **norms** are examples of a quite sophisticated mathematical notion of measurement of distance and will be totally unfamiliar at this stage.

9

All that is required here is a very superficial understanding of their meaning and purpose.

The first of these measures the extreme discrepancy between f and the approximant p while the others are both measures of the 'total discrepancy' over the interval. Of course, if all we know are the values of f at the points $x_0, x_1, \ldots, x_n$, then the corresponding **discrete** versions of these measures must be used, namely

$$\max_{x_i} |f(x_i) - p(x_i)|,$$

$$\sum_{i=0}^{n} |f(x_i) - p(x_i)|$$

or

$$\left(\sum_{i=0}^{n} |f(x_i) - p(x_i)|^2 \right)^{1/2}.$$

The last of these is the measure of total error commonly used in obtaining a least-squares fit to experimental data.

In these cases where we have data at just a finite set of points we can use polynomial interpolation (chapter 4) to obtain a polynomial p such that $f(x_i) = p(x_i)$ for each x_i and so make any of these measures of error zero. However, this may not be such a good idea as it may at first appear. Firstly, the data may well be subject to experimental errors so that fitting it exactly is merely perpetuating such errors; secondly, information on the form of f may tell us from which class of functions to choose p; thirdly, if there are many data points, we do not wish to compute a very-high-degree polynomial in full.

1.5 FLOATING-POINT ARITHMETIC

In this section, we discuss very briefly the error analysis of floating-point arithmetic and some of its implications for computer design. For completeness, we shall present the results for an arbitrary base β which is in practice almost invariably $\beta = 2$ (binary) or 16 (hexadecimal) for a computer or $\beta = 10$ (decimal) for a hand-calculator.

A positive number x will be represented in normalised floating-point form by

$$\hat{x} = \hat{f} \beta^E, \tag{1.3}$$

where the fraction $\hat{f}$ consists of a fixed number, k say, of base-β digits, that is,

$$\hat{f} = 0 . \hat{d}_1 \hat{d}_2 \ldots \hat{d}_k, \tag{1.4}$$

where $1 \leqslant \hat{d}_1 \leqslant \beta - 1$ and $0 \leqslant \hat{d}_i \leqslant \beta - 1$ for $i = 2, 3, \ldots, k$.

The absolute error in representing $x = f\beta^E$ where

$$f = 0.d_1 d_2 \ldots$$

$$= \sum_{i=1}^{\infty} d_i \beta^{-i} \tag{1.5}$$

by $\hat{x}$ is therefore

$$|x - \hat{x}| = \beta^E |f - \hat{f}|. \tag{1.6}$$

If $\hat{f}$ is obtained from f by chopping then $\hat{d}_i = d_i$ for $i = 1, 2, \ldots, k$ and so

$$|x - \hat{x}| = \beta^E \sum_{i=k+1}^{\infty} d_i \beta^{-i}. \tag{1.7}$$

For symmetric rounding, we add $\beta/2$ to d_{k+1} and then chop the result so that

$$|x - \hat{x}| = \beta^E \left| \sum_{i=k+1}^{\infty} d_i \beta^{-i} - \frac{\beta^{-k}}{2} \right|. \tag{1.8}$$

Of more interest for floating-point calculations is the size of the relative error

$$\frac{|x - \hat{x}|}{|x|} = \frac{|f - \hat{f}|}{|f|}.$$

For the quantities given by equations (1.4) and (1.5), we find that

$$\frac{|f - \hat{f}|}{|f|} \leqslant \begin{cases} \dfrac{1}{\beta^{k-1}} & \text{for chopping,} \\[2mm] \dfrac{1}{2\beta^{k-1}} & \text{for rounding.} \end{cases} \tag{1.9}$$

We prove the 'chopping' result and leave the 'rounding' case as an exercise for the reader. By definition,

$$\frac{|f - \hat{f}|}{|f|} = \left(\sum_{i=k+1}^{\infty} d_i \beta^{-i} \right) \Big/ |f|$$

$$\leqslant \frac{\beta^{-k}}{|f|}$$

$$\leqslant \beta^{1-k},$$

as required, since $f \leqslant 1/\beta$ and $d_i \leqslant \beta - 1$ for each i.

Now let $\circ$ stand for one of the elementary arithmetic operations $+$, $-$, $\times$ or $\div$ and suppose that x and y are *exactly* represented by their floating-point forms. If the arithmetic is performed in such a way that all figures which can affect the result of $x \circ y$ are taken into account before abbreviation takes place (whether by chopping or rounding), then the rounding error bounds of equation (1.9) are preserved.

11

Two important observations on this are that the proviso for accuracy above requires the use of double-length representation of the fractions in the arithmetic unit and that it says nothing (or very little) about the genuine accuracy of floating-point arithmetic. For this, we need bounds on the quantity

$$\frac{|(\hat{x} \circ \hat{y})^{\hat{}} - x \circ y|}{|x \circ y|}$$

and not just

$$\frac{|(x \circ y)^{\hat{}} - x \circ y|}{|x \circ y|}.$$

Such bounds will vary with the nature of the operation $\circ$.

Example 1.5.1

For subtraction of nearly equal numbers the relative rounding error may be large. Let $x = 0.123\,44$, $y = 0.123\,51$ and suppose that we compute their difference using a four-decimal-digit floating-point representation. Then

$$\hat{x} = 0.1234$$

$$\hat{y} = 0.1235$$

and

$$(\hat{x} - \hat{y})^{\hat{}} = \hat{x} - \hat{y}$$

$$= -0.0001$$

$$= -0.1000 \times 10^{-3}$$

while

$$x - y = -0.7 \times 10^{-4},$$

so that the relative rounding error is

$$\frac{10^{-4}(1.0 - 0.7)}{0.7 \times 10^{-4}} = \frac{3}{7}$$

$$\approx 0.4286.$$

That is, there is an error of about 43%.

The next example, this time in terms of absolute errors, illustrates a common drawback of simplistic error bounds.

Example 1.5.2

Using 'exact' arithmetic, we see that

$$\tfrac{1}{11} + \tfrac{1}{12} + \ldots + \tfrac{1}{20} = 0.668\ 771 \text{ to six decimal places}$$

but that, rounding each of the terms to four decimal places, we obtain the approximate value 0.6687. Thus the accumulated rounding error is only about 7×10^{-5} whereas at each stage the error is bounded by 5×10^{-5} so that the accumulative error bound obtained is 5×10^{-4}—that is, about seven times the actual error committed.

This phenomenon is by no means unusual and leads to the study of probabilistic error analyses for floating-point calculations. For such analyses to be reliable, it is necessary to have a good model for the distribution of numbers as they arise in practice within scientific computing. It is a well-established fact that the fractions of floating-point numbers are logarithmically distributed. One immediate implication of this distribution is the rather surprising statement that the proportion of (base-β) floating-point numbers with leading significant digit n is given by

$$\frac{\log(n + 1) - \log n}{\log \beta}.$$

In particular, 30% of decimal numbers have a leading significant digit 1 while only about $4\tfrac{1}{2}\%$ have a leading significant digit 9.

This chapter has provided a very superficial overview of an extensive subject and has, I hope, raised at least as many questions in your mind as it has answered.

EXERCISES 1.5

1 Express the base of natural logarithms e as a normalised floating-point number using

   (a) base 10 and four digits,
   (b) base 2 and 10 bits and
   (c) base 16 and three hexadecimal digits.

2 Carry out the calculation of Example 1.3.1 and repeat it with chopping on a six-decimal-digit machine.

3 Write a computer program to estimate the **machine epsilon** for your computer. Machine epsilon is the smallest positive machine number ε for

which $1 + \varepsilon > 1$. Try taking $\varepsilon = 10^{-k}$ and 2^{-k} for increasing values of k. Are the two values which you obtained equal?

4 Write a computer program to 'sum' the series

$$1 + \tfrac{1}{2} + \tfrac{1}{3} + \ldots$$

stopping when

(a) all subsequent terms are zero to three decimal places and
(b) two successive estimates of the sum are equal to machine accuracy.

How many terms are needed in each case? How many terms would be needed before the next one is zero to machine accuracy? Why is this number different from that for (b)?

5 For what range of values of x will the truncation error in approximating $\exp x$ by $\sum_{n=0}^{6} x^n/n!$ be bounded by 10^{-10}?

6 Suppose that the exponential function $\exp x$ is approximated on the interval $[0, 1]$ by the function $1 + x$. Find the measure of the error in this approximation in the L_∞, L_1 and L_2 metrics.

7 Try to convince yourself of the validity of the statement that floating-point numbers are logarithmically distributed using the following experiment. Write a program which can find the leading significant (decimal) digit of a number in $[0, 1)$. (Hint: keep multiplying the number by 10 until it is in $[1, 10)$ and then take its integer part.) Use the random-number generator to obtain uniformly distributed numbers in the interval $[0, 1)$. Form 1000 products of pairs of such numbers and find how many of these have leading significant digits $1, 2, \ldots, 9$. Repeat this with products of three, four and five such factors. If you have a hexadecimal machine, repeat this exercise to find the distribution of the leading hexadecimal digits.

2 ITERATIVE SOLUTION OF EQUATIONS; CONVERGENCE OF SEQUENCES

2.1 INTRODUCTION

In this chapter, we are concerned with the problem of solving an equation of the form

$$f(x) = 0. \qquad (2.1)$$

The basic principle of our methods is to generate a **sequence** of estimates of the required solution which we hope **converges** to this solution. It will therefore be necessary to study exactly what is meant by these terms and this is done later in this chapter. A much fuller treatment of the convergence of sequences has been given by Hawkins (1988).

The principle of iterative methods is that an initial estimate, or guess, of the solution is made and this is then continually refined (usually according to some simple rule) in such a way that the subsequent estimates, or **iterates**, get steadily closer to the required solution of the original problem. Because of the repetitious nature of the calculations, such methods are well suited to implementation on a computer. Some sample programs are included.

It is worth making a few general remarks about these programs in advance. Firstly, they are not intended to be robust general-purpose programs but simply to illustrate the methods described in the text. Secondly, in all cases, they are written in such a way as to solve a particular example problem and so would need some modifications for other examples. Thirdly, and perhaps most importantly, these programs are written in a powerful form of BASIC such as might be found on a mainframe system rather than on many microcomputers. For use on such a machine many more line numbers would be needed, the IF...THEN...ELSE... constructs may need to be replaced by branching statements and the creation of output files would not be wanted. The main reason for using these facilities here is that the underlying structure of a program is more evident. It may also serve as a useful step in the transition from BASIC to higher-level scientific programming languages such as FORTRAN.

2.2 THE METHOD OF BISECTION

Perhaps the simplest technique for solving equation (2.1) is to use the **method of bisection** which is based on a commonsense application of the **intermediate-value theorem**.

Suppose that f is continuous and that for two points $a < b$:

$$f(a) < 0 < f(b).$$

Then, by the intermediate-value theorem, there is a solution of equation (2.1) between a and b. Now, if c is the midpoint of $[a, b]$, that is,

$$c = \frac{a+b}{2}, \tag{2.2}$$

and, if $f(c) > 0$, then, again using the intermediate-value theorem, there is a solution in (a, c) while, if $f(c) < 0$, then there is a solution in (c, b) (see Fig. 2.1). In either case therefore we have a new interval containing the solution which is half the length of the previous one. There is of course a similar statement for the situation $f(a) > 0 > f(b)$. We can repeat this process until the solution has been found to any required accuracy. If h is this **tolerance**, then once $b - a < h$ we are done; otherwise we replace either b or a by c and continue.

The procedure is summarised in the flow chart in Fig. 2.2.

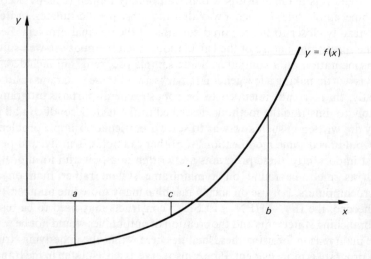

Fig. 2.1 The bisection method. In this case $f(c) < 0$; a is replaced by c for the next iteration

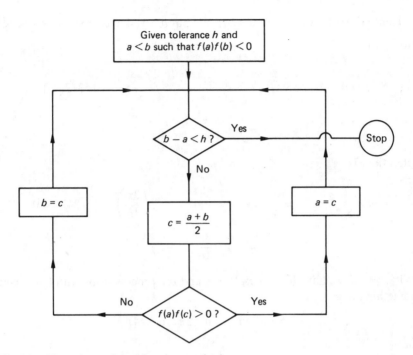

Fig. 2.2 Flow chart of the bisection method

Example 2.2.1

Consider the equation $x = \cos x$ or

$$x - \cos x = 0. \tag{2.3}$$

Writing $f(x) = x - \cos x$, we have

$$f(0) = -1 < 0$$

and

$$f\left(\frac{\pi}{2}\right) = \frac{\pi}{2} > 0.$$

Since f is continuous, it follows that there is a solution of equation (2.3) in $[0, \pi/2]$. Then, using the method of bisection, we get

(iteration 1)

$$a = 0, \qquad b = \frac{\pi}{2} \quad \Rightarrow \quad c = \frac{\pi}{4}, \qquad f\left(\frac{\pi}{4}\right) = 0.0783 > 0.$$

17

Hence the solution lies in $(0, \pi/4)$. We put $b = \pi/4$ and repeat the process: (iteration 2)

$$a = 0, \qquad b = \frac{\pi}{4} \quad \Rightarrow \quad c = \frac{\pi}{8}, \qquad f\left(\frac{\pi}{8}\right) = -0.5312 < 0,$$

$$\Rightarrow \quad a = \frac{\pi}{8},$$

(iteration 3)

$$a = \frac{\pi}{8}, \qquad b = \frac{\pi}{4} \quad \Rightarrow \quad c = \frac{3\pi}{16}, \qquad f\left(\frac{3\pi}{16}\right) = -0.2424 < 0,$$

$$\Rightarrow \quad a = \frac{3\pi}{16}.$$

With $h = 0.2$ we have $b - a = \pi/16 < h$ and the process stops with a message something like

Solution lies in $(3\pi/16, \pi/4)$

or

Solution is 0.6872 with error less than 0.1

(note that 0.6872 is the midpoint of $(3\pi/16, \pi/4)$ and so is less than $h/2$ away from either end).

The following program illustrates the use of the method of bisection for the solution of

$$\exp x - 2x - 1 = 0 \qquad (2.4)$$

This equation, like equation (2.3), will be used as a standard example for the various iterative methods that we discuss.

PROGRAM 2.2.1

```
1    REM ****** SOLUTION OF EQUATION F(X) = 0 BY BISECTION ******
10 OPEN "RESULTS." FOR OUTPUT AS FILE £3
     DEF FNF(X) = EXP(X) − 2*X − 1
     PRINT £3, "SOLUTION OF EQUATION F(X) = 0 BY METHOD OF BISECTION"
     PRINT £3, "F(X) = EXP(X) − 2*X − 1"
     PRINT "PUT IN THE REQUIRED TOLERANCE"
     INPUT H
     PRINT £3, "ACCURACY REQUIRED IS"; H
     PRINT £3,
```

```
20  PRINT "PUT IN TWO STARTING VALUES A < B"
    INPUT A,B
    FA = FNF(A) \ FB = FNF(B)
    PRINT £3, "INITIAL VALUES"
    PRINT £3, "A = "; A, "F(A) = "; FA
    PRINT £3, "B = "; B, "F(B) = "; FB
    PRINT £3,

30  IF FA*FB > 0 THEN PRINT £3, "INITIAL VALUES HAVE SAME SIGN"
                      PRINT £3, \ PRINT £3,
                      PRINT "VALUES HAVE SAME SIGN"
                      GOTO 20

40  C = (A + B)/2 \ FC = FNF(C)
    IF FA*FC > 0 THEN A = C \ FA = FC
              ELSE B = C \ FB = FC

50  IF B − A > H THEN 40
                 ELSE PRINT £3, "CONVERGED TO REQUIRED TOLERANCE"
                      PRINT £3, "FINAL INTERVAL: A = "; A, "B = "; B
                      PRINT £3, "F(A) = "; FA, "F(B) = "; FB

60  STOP
    END
```

Remarks

(a) The two different types of 'print' statement are used for printing on the screen (using the PRINT command) to ask for input or to give the user messages while PRINT £3 is used for information which is to be included in the final output from the program. The symbol \ is used to separate two different instructions on the same line of the program.

(b) Note the inclusion of a test to check (line 30) that the initial values given to the computer do indeed lie either side of the required solution. If this is not the case, then an appropriate message is printed on the terminal screen and the program returns to line 20 to ask for further input. (In fact, of course, these conditions ensure that there are an odd number of solutions in the interval; the method can then be guaranteed to converge to one of them.)

Example 2.2.2

Solve the equation

$$\exp x - 2x - 1 = 0$$

using Program 2.2.1.

With tolerance $H = 1E - 4$ (that is, 10^{-4}) and initial input $A = 0$ and $B = 1$ we get the message

VALUES HAVE SAME SIGN

on the screen followed by a request for another set of initial values to be typed in. With A = 1 and B = 2 the program will run successfully and the final output will look like this:

SOLUTION OF EQUATION F(X) = 0 BY BISECTION
F(X) = EXP(X) − 2∗X − 1

ACCURACY REQUIRED IS .0001

INITIAL VALUES
A = 0   F(A) = − 1
B = 1   F(B) = − .281718

INITIAL VALUES HAVE SAME SIGN

INITIAL VALUES
A = 1   F(A) = − .281718
B = 2   F(B) = 2.38906

CONVERGED TO REQUIRED TOLERANCE
FINAL INTERVAL: A = 1.25641   B = 1.25647
F(A) = − .340939E − 04   F(B) = .581741E − 04

Note the sort of information which is included in the output. Obviously the intention is to provide the user with as much *useful* information as possible without burying him or her in reams of paper. You should also note that virtually all the real work is being done by the single line, line 40, of the program together with the first part of line 50 which asks the question, 'Have we finished?' and returns the program to line 40 if the answer is 'No'. The actual computation is seen therefore to be very simple in this case.

The proof that this algorithm converges—that is, the sequence of points generated converges to the solution—will be a simple application of the **sandwich rule** for convergence of sequences (see section 2.5).

EXERCISES 2.2

1 Show that the equation

$$3x^3 - 5x^2 - 4x + 4 = 0$$

has a root in the interval [0, 1]. Use the method of bisection to find an interval of length $\frac{1}{8}$ containing this solution.

How many evaluations of the functions $3x^3 - 5x^2 - 4x + 4$ would be needed to obtain the solution with an error less than 10^{-6} by this method?

2 Show that the equation

$$\exp x - 100x^2 = 0$$

has exactly three solutions and find intervals of length less than 0.1 containing them.

2.3 SIMPLE ITERATION

In the last section, we saw that bisection provides a simple and reliable technique for solving an equation which is probably sufficient for any relatively straightforward one-off problem. However, if the function f is itself more complicated (perhaps its values must be obtained from the numerical solution of some differential equation, say) or if the task is to be performed repeatedly for different values of some parameters, then a more efficient method may well be desirable.

If equation (2.1) is rewritten in the form

$$x = g(x) \tag{2.5}$$

then this **rearrangement** can be used to define an iterative process as follows. We make a guess at the solution, x_0 say, and use this to define a **sequence** (x_n) by

$$x_n = g(x_{n-1}) \qquad n = 1, 2, \dots . \tag{2.6}$$

Now, provided that g is continuous, we see that, *if* this sequence converges, then the terms get closer and closer together and eventually we obtain

$$x_n \approx x_{n-1}$$

or, in other words,

$$x_{n-1} \approx g(x_{n-1}).$$

That is, x_{n-1} is, approximately, a solution of equation (2.5).

Example 2.3.1

Again consider the equation $x - \cos x = 0$ which we rearrange as

$$x = \cos x$$

so that we use the **iteration function** $g(x) = \cos x$.

We have already seen in Example 2.2.1 that the solution lies in $(3\pi/16, \pi/4)$ and so we might choose $x_0 = 0.7$ from which we get the subsequent values

$$x_1 = 0.7648,$$

$$x_2 = 0.7215,$$

$$x_3 = 0.7508,$$

$$x_4 = 0.7311,$$

$$\vdots$$

$$x_9 = 0.7402,$$

$$x_{10} = 0.7383,$$

$$x_{11} = 0.7396,$$

from which we might conclude that the solution is 0.74 to two decimal places.

However, note that we have *proved nothing* about the convergence of this iteration.

Certainly such an approach will not always be successful as we can see from the alternative iteration $x_n = \cos^{-1}(x_{n-1})$. Using the very good starting point $x_0 = 0.74$, the next few iterates generated are

0.7377, 0.7411, 0.7361, 0.7435, 0.7325, 0.7489, 0.7245, 0.7605,

0.7067, 0.7860, 0.6665, 0.8414, 0.5710, 0.9631, 0.2727, 1.2946,

so that after 16 iterations the next iterate is not even defined!

(To check these numbers, note that in the first case all that is needed is to press the cos button on your calculator repeatedly after putting in the starting point 0.7 *in radians*. The second case uses the inverse cosine function.)

As was said above, we have not established anything about the convergence of iterative schemes—perhaps not surprisingly since we have not yet defined the term precisely. However, we can obtain some conditions for this convergence quite simply.

Firstly, $x = g(x)$ must be a rearrangement of the original equation $f(x) = 0$. Therefore, these two equations must be equivalent; that is, we must have

$$f(x) = 0 \Leftrightarrow x = g(x).$$

Also, consideration of the Taylor series of g about the solution s gives us

$$
\begin{aligned}
x_{n+1} - s &= g(x_n) - s \\
&= g(x_n) - g(s) \\
&= g(s) + (x_n - s)g'(s) + \frac{(x_n - s)^2 g''(s)}{2} + \ldots - g(s) \\
&= (x_n - s)g'(s) + \frac{(x_n - s)^2 g''(s)}{2} + \ldots.
\end{aligned}
$$

Now, if $x_n - s$ is small enough that higher-order terms can be neglected, we have

$$x_{n+1} - s \approx (x_n - s)g'(s) \qquad (2.7)$$

and so we see that the error will be reduced provided that

$$|g'(s)| < 1. \tag{2.8}$$

Of course, at the beginning of the iterative process, we do not know the solution and so cannot apply this result directly. We shall see later that a sufficient condition for the convergence of the iteration (2.6) is that for some interval $[a, b]$ containing the solution s

$$x \in [a, b] \Rightarrow g(x) \in [a, b] \qquad \text{and} \qquad |g'(x)| < 1.$$

Example 2.3.2

Consider equation (2.4), $\exp x - 2x - 1 = 0$, which we know from Example 2.2.2 has a solution in $[1, 2]$.

One simple rearrangement of this is

$$x = \frac{\exp x - 1}{2} \tag{2.9}$$

Now the iteration function $g(x) = (\exp x - 1)/2$ is increasing since its derivative is $g'(x) = (\exp x)/2$ which is positive everywhere. Hence for any value $x > \log 5 \approx 1.6094$ we obtain $g(x) > [\exp(\log 5) - 1]/2 = 2$ and so the above condition is not satisfied. Indeed this iteration will not converge to the solution for any starting point other than the solution itself!

If, however, we rewrite equation (2.4) as $\exp x = 2x + 1$ and take logarithms of both sides, we get the equation

$$x = \log(2x + 1). \tag{2.10}$$

Using this as the iteration function, we find that $g'(x) = 2/(2x + 1)$ which lies between $\frac{2}{5}$ and $\frac{2}{3}$ for any $x \in [1, 2]$. Thus, g is again increasing and, since $g(1) = \log 3$ and $g(2) = \log 5$, it follows that the above conditions are satisfied and the iteration will converge for any starting point in $[1, 2]$.

This iteration is implemented in Program 2.3.1 below. On this occasion, READ and DATA have been used for the starting point and the tolerance. Again nearly all the work is done in a small section of the program, namely the loop from line 20 to line 30 in which the previous values of X0 and X1 are overwritten in turn by X1 and X2 and then the next iterate X2 is generated using the iteration function by X2 = FNG(X1). For this particular implementation a maximum of 50 iterations have been allowed and, if this were exceeded, the program would stop with an appropriate message.

The convergence criterion used here is that *three* successive iterates must agree to within the required tolerance. Without a very detailed error analysis of an iterative scheme, it is usually difficult to determine at what point the computation should stop and the answer be accepted as correct. Generally speaking, the agreement of two successive iterates is not quite enough although insisting on the agreement of three may be a rather oversevere test. It is also worth noting that the statement $X1 = X2 - 2*H$ in line 20 will guarantee that the convergence test cannot be satisfied after just one iteration.

In this case the output tells us that the process converges in 12 iterations and the final three iterates are

$$1.255\,32, \qquad 1.255\,80, \qquad 1.256\,07,$$

which leads us to the likely conclusion that the solution is about 1.256; we would certainly seem to be justified in assuming that this result has an error less than 0.001, the tolerance given in the program. However, again we have *proved nothing* about the accuracy of this result.

PROGRAM 2.3.1

```
1   REM ******SOLUTION OF EQUATION F(X) = 0 BY ITERATION ******
10  OPEN "RESULTS." FOR OUTPUT AS FILE £3
    PRINT £3, "SOLUTION OF EQUATION F(X) = 0 BY ITERATION"
    PRINT £3, "F(X) = EXP(X) − 2X − 1"
    PRINT £3, "ITERATION FUNCTION USED IS G(X)"
    PRINT £3, "G(X) = LOG(1 + 2X)"
    DEF FNG(X) = LOG(1 + 2*X)
    READ X2,H
    PRINT £3, "ACCURACY REQUIRED IS"; H
    PRINT £3, "INITIAL POINT IS"; X2

20  X1 = X2 − 2*H
    FOR I = 1 TO 50
       X0 = X1 \ X1 = X2
       X2 = FNG(X1)
       IF ABS(X1 − X0) < H AND ABS(X2 − X0) < H AND ABS(X2 − X1) < H THEN 50

30  NEXT I

40  PRINT £3, "FAILED TO CONVERGE IN 50 ITERATIONS"
    GOTO 60

50  PRINT £3, "CONVERGED IN"; I; "ITERATIONS"
    PRINT £3, "LAST THREE ITERATES:"; X0, X1, X2

60  STOP
70  DATA 1, 1E − 3
80  END
```

The progress of iterative schemes such as these is easily illustrated, as in Fig. 2.3. These diagrams represent the procedure whereby for each x_n we obtain the value $y = g(x_n)$ and then the next iterate x_{n+1} is read off from the

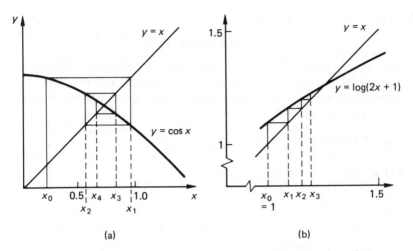

Fig. 2.3 Function iteration: (a) $x = \cos x$; (b) $x = \log(2x + 1)$

graph of $y = x$. It is fairly easy to see from the figures that the condition $|g'(x)| < 1$ over some interval containing all the iterates and the solution is sufficient to ensure that this process converges to the solution which is of course situated where the two graphs intersect. Similar pictures with $|g'(x)| > 1$ will readily show that, even with a very good initial guess x_0, the iteration would produce a sequence of points moving rapidly away from the required solution.

EXERCISES 2.3

1 The equation

$$3x^3 - 5x^2 - 4x + 4 = 0$$

has a root near $x = 0.7$. Decide which of the following rearrangements result in a convergent iteration for locating this root.

(a) $x = \dfrac{5}{3} + \dfrac{4}{3x} - \dfrac{4}{3x^2}$.

(b) $x = 1 + \dfrac{3x^3 - 5x^2}{4}$.

(c) $x = \sqrt{\dfrac{3x^3 - 4x + 4}{5}}$.

Modify Program 2.3.1 to find this solution using whichever of these you chose. Set the tolerance to 10^{-6}. Compare the number of iterations with the predicted number of bisection iterations in Exercises 2.2, **1**.

25

2 In Exercises 2.2, **2**, we saw that the equation

$$\exp x - 100x^2 = 0$$

has three solutions. Each of the following rearrangements will provide a convergent iteration for one of these solutions. Verify that they are all rearrangements of the original equation and determine which will converge to which solution.

(a) $x = \dfrac{\exp(x/2)}{10}$.

(b) $x = 2(\ln x + \ln 10)$.

(c) $x = \dfrac{-\exp(x/2)}{10}$.

Use the appropriate iterations in Program 2.3.1 to obtain the solutions to five decimal places.

2.4 NEWTON'S METHOD

If we again consider the approximate equation (2.7) obtained from the Taylor series of the iteration function g, we see that the error $x_{n+1} - s$ will be reduced rapidly if the derivative $g'(s)$ is small. This is the motivation for **Newton's** or the **Newton–Raphson method**.

Returning to the original equation $f(x) = 0$ (which was equation (2.1)) and using the Taylor series of this function about a point x_0, we have

$$f(x) = f(x_0) + (x - x_0)f'(x_0) + \frac{(x - x_0)^2}{2}f''(x_0) + \dots. \qquad (2.11)$$

If we assume again that all second- and higher-order terms are negligible, then we get

$$f(x) \approx f(x_0) + (x - x_0)f'(x_0) \qquad (2.12)$$

and setting the right-hand side to zero should give a better estimate of the solution. Thus we take

$$x_1 = x_0 - \frac{f(x_0)}{f'(x_0)}.$$

Repeating this argument leads to the iteration

$$x_{n+1} = x_n - \frac{f(x_n)}{f'(x_n)} \qquad n = 0, 1, 2, \dots. \qquad (2.13)$$

This is Newton's method which therefore uses the iteration function

$$g(x) = x - \frac{f(x)}{f'(x)}. \qquad (2.14)$$

Differentiating this function, we see that

$$g'(x) = 1 - \frac{f'(x)}{f'(x)} + \frac{f(x)f''(x)}{[f'(x)]^2}$$

$$= \frac{f(x)f''(x)}{[f'(x)]^2}$$

and, since $f(s) = 0$, it follows that $g'(s) = 0$, which we suggested above is likely to produce rapid improvement in the accuracy of the iterates.

This method has a simple graphical representation (Fig. 2.4).

Newton's method is widely used within computers for the evaluation of square roots and even reciprocals.

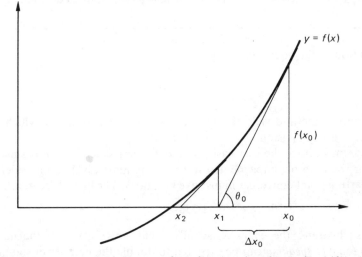

Fig. 2.4 Newton's method. Here $\tan \theta_0 = f'(x_0)$ and so $\Delta x_0 = f(x_0)/f'(x_0)$. Thus x_1 is the point at which the tangent to the curve $y = f(x)$ at $x = x_0$ cuts the x axis

---

Example 2.4.1

Find the positive square root of a real number c.

We wish to solve the equation

$$x^2 - c = 0$$

and the Newton iteration is therefore

$$x_{n+1} = x_n - \frac{(x_n^2 - c)}{2x_n}$$

$$= \frac{(x_n + c/x_n)}{2}.$$

27

We shall consider the general convergence properties of Newton's method later but for now simply comment that this iteration is convergent for every choice of $x_0 > 0$.

For example, take $c = 5$ and $x_0 = 2$. We get

$$x_1 = \frac{2 + \frac{5}{2}}{2}$$

$$= 2.25,$$

$$x_2 = 2.236\,111,$$

$$x_3 = 2.236\,068 \qquad \text{(agreement to three decimal places already)},$$

$$x_4 = 2.236\,068 \qquad \text{(which is indeed correct to six decimal places)}.$$

Solution of the equation

$$\frac{1}{x} - c = 0$$

by Newton's method yields an iterative scheme for finding $1/c$ which does not involve any division.

Program 2.3.1 can be very easily adapted to implement Newton's method and for the example implemented in that program with the same tolerance and starting point converges in just five iterations. The final three iterates are

$$1.256\,78, \qquad 1.256\,43, \qquad 1.256\,43.$$

This illustrates the characteristically rapid convergence of the method which *roughly speaking* can be expected to double the number of significant figures accuracy on each iteration—*when it works*.

Newton's method will not always work, however. Consideration of equation (2.13) shows that, if $f'(x_n)$ is very small, then the correction made to the iterate x_n will be very large. Thus, if the derivative of f is zero (or very small) near the solution, then the iteration is unlikely to be successful. Such a situation could arise if there are two solutions very close together or, as in Fig. 2.5, when the gradient of f is small everywhere except very close to the solution.

Example 2.4.2

Consider the equation $\tan^{-1}(x - 1) = 0.5$ which has the solution $x = 1.5463$ to four decimal places.

The function $\tan^{-1}(x - 1) - 0.5$ has a graph similar to that illustrated in Fig. 2.3. Newton's method with the rather poor starting point $x_0 = 4$ then

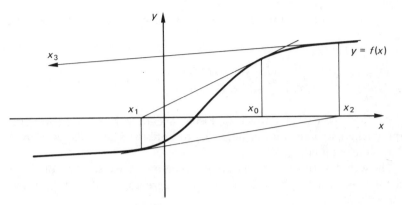

Fig. 2.5 Newton's method can fail

gives $x_1 \approx -3.49$ and $x_2 \approx 35.7$. If allowed to continue, the oscillations of the iterates get steadily wilder until eventually the program would fail through overflow.

(Of course, it should be noted that this is a very silly way to proceed for this particular equation which could be rewritten as $x = 1 + \tan(0.5)$ and so can be solved very simply using the computer's standard routine for evaluating the tangent function. We thus change the problem from one of equation solving to one of function evaluation—but this is still a real numerical problem as we shall see in later chapters.)

The observation has already been made that Program 2.3.1 can easily be adapted to implement Newton's method. However, this requires that the derivative f' is known. In practice, this may not be possible as the equation may itself be obtained as the result of some other computational process and we may not even have a precise formula for its values. In such circumstances the power of Newton's method is unavailable. The **secant method** is an attempt to recover some of that power without the need for the derivative function itself.

We observed in Fig. 2.4 that the iterate x_{n+1} of Newton's method is the point at which the tangent at x_n meets the axis. For the secant method, we use instead the chord joining the points on the graph corresponding to the last two iterates. The method thus needs two initial guesses x_0 and x_1.

The equation of the chord joining the points $(x_0, f(x_0))$ and $(x_1, f(x_1))$ is

$$y - f(x_0) = \frac{f(x_1) - f(x_0)}{x_1 - x_0}(x - x_0), \tag{2.15}$$

and setting $y = 0$ in (2.15) gives us the following expression for the next iterate:

$$x_2 = \frac{x_0 f(x_1) - x_1 f(x_0)}{f(x_1) - f(x_0)}.$$

29

The general formula for generating subsequent points in this sequence is therefore

$$x_{n+1} = \frac{x_{n-1}f(x_n) - x_n f(x_{n-1})}{f(x_n) - f(x_{n-1})} \qquad n = 1, 2, 3, \ldots .$$

Note that there is a danger of losing accuracy here as convergence is approached, so that it may be necessary to work to a higher degree of accuracy than that required.

The secant method can also be regarded as an implementation of Newton's method in which we replace the true derivative value $f'(x_1)$ by the approximation

$$\frac{f(x_1) - f(x_0)}{x_1 - x_0}.$$

This is about the simplest possible approximation to this derivative and is sufficient for the present purposes. (Although **numerical differentiation** is a notoriously difficult problem best avoided where possible, its use here, where the actual *value* of the derivative is of secondary importance, is justifiable.)

Example 2.4.3

We know from Example 2.2.1 that the equation $x - \cos x = 0$ has a solution in $(3\pi/16, \pi/4)$. The secant method with $x_0 = 0.6$ and $x_1 = 0.8$ gives

$$f(x_0) = -0.2253,$$
$$f(x_1) = 0.1033,$$

from which we get $x_2 = 0.7371$ and $f(x_2) = -3.321 \times 10^{-3}$. The next two iterations yield $x_3 = 0.7390$ and $f(x_3) = -1.425 \times 10^{-4}$ and then $x_4 = 0.7391$ which is accurate to four decimal places.

Although this method does not have quite such rapid convergence as Newton's method, it can be expected to provide high levels of accuracy fairly quickly.

The secant method for solving the equation of Examples 2.2.2 and 2.3.2 is implemented in the following program. It is worth noting that we do not call on the function definition for the new iterate X2 until we know that another iteration will be required—by which time this point has been relabelled X1.

PROGRAM 2.4.1

```
1   REM ****** SOLUTION OF EQUATION F(X) = 0 BY SECANT METHOD ******
10  OPEN "RESULTS." FOR OUTPUT AS FILE £3
    PRINT £3, "SOLUTION OF EQUATION F(X) = 0 BY SECANT METHOD"
    PRINT £3, "F(X) = EXP(X) − 2X − 1"
    DEF FNF(X) = EXP(X) − 2*X − 1
    READ H, X0, X1
    PRINT £3, "ACCURACY REQUIRED IS"; H
    PRINT £3, "INITIAL POINTS ARE"; X0; "AND"; X1
    F0 = FNF(X0) \ F1 = FNF(X1)

20  FOR I = 1 TO 50
        X2 = (X0*F1 − X1*F0)/(F1 − F0)
        IF ABS(X1 − X0) < H AND ABS(X2 − X0) < H AND ABS(X2 − X1) < H THEN 60
30      X0 = X1 \ X1 = X2 \ F0 = F1 \ F1 = FNF(X1)
40  NEXT I

50  PRINT £3, "FAILED TO CONVERGE IN 50 ITERATIONS"
    GOTO 70

60  PRINT £3, "CONVERGED IN"; I; "ITERATIONS"
    PRINT £3, "LAST THREE ITERATES:"; X0, X1, X2
70  STOP
80  DATA 1E − 3, 1, 2
90  END
```

The output from this program shows that it converges in seven iterations with the last three being 1.256 39, 1.256 43 and 1.256 43.

Frequently, we have made reference to the notion of a sequence *converging* to the solution of an equation with, as yet, at best a rough idea of the meaning of this term. The next few sections are devoted to gaining a clearer understanding of this. It is worth pointing out too that in many practical situations it would be helpful to use a hybrid algorithm which might, for example, use bisection as a reliable way of obtaining a small interval containing the solution and then Newton's method to refine the estimated solution to the required accuracy.

EXERCISES 2.4

1   Modify Program 2.3.1 for the solution of an equation by Newton's method. Use this to obtain the three solutions of $\exp x - 100x^2 = 0$. Note that there are two solutions near $x = 0$ and so care must be taken over the starting points for these cases. Try to find experimentally the 'critical point' c such that, if $x_0 > c$, then the solution near 0.1 is obtained while, if $x_0 < c$, the negative solution is obtained. Now try to justify this behaviour theoretically.

2 Repeat the computation of the previous example using the secant method, Program 2.4.1. What happens if the two starting points straddle the 'critical point' found for Newton's method?

3 Show that using Newton's method to find reciprocals—that is, to solve $1/x - c = 0$—results in the iteration

$$x_{n+1} = x_n(2 - cx_n).$$

Show that the iteration function g used here satisfies $|g'(x)| < 1$ for all $x \in (1/2c, 3/2c)$.

We shall see later that this implies convergence of this iteration provided that the initial guess is in error by no more than 50%. To find the reciprocal of a normalised binary number, we require $1/c$ where $c = f \times 2^E$ and $f \in [\frac{1}{2}, 1)$. It follows that $1/c = (1/f) \times 2^{-E}$ and on normalising this becomes

$$\frac{1}{c} = \left(\frac{1}{2f}\right) \times 2^{1-E}.$$

The problem is thus reduced to obtaining the reciprocal of $2f$ which we know lies in $[\frac{1}{2}, 1)$. Newton's method with $x_0 = \frac{3}{4}$ can be used to find this very quickly. This is the basis of several routines for floating-point division in machines where there is no such hardware operation.

2.5 CONVERGENCE OF SEQUENCES

We begin by trying to answer the following question.

What does it mean to say that the sequence (x_n) converges to l as n tends to infinity?

Certainly, we must have that x_n 'gets closer' to l as n becomes large—but $1/n$ 'gets closer' to *any* negative number and so this cannot be enough. One of the notions which we used was that, if an iteration carried on long enough, then we could get approximations of any required accuracy to the solution. Thus the definition must include the idea that x_n gets 'arbitrarily close' to l for large enough n—and *it stays there*.

DEFINITION 2.5.1   The sequence (x_n) *converges* (tends) to the *limit l* as n tends to infinity, written

$$x_n \to l \qquad \text{as} \qquad n \to \infty$$

or

$$\lim_{n \to \infty} x_n = l$$

if for every number $h > 0$ there exists an integer N (usually dependent on h) such that $|x_n - l| < h$ whenever $n > N$ or, equivalently, $l - h < x_n < l + h$ whenever $n > N$.

Thus, for any given tolerance h, if we go far enough along the sequence, we reach a point beyond which *all* subsequent terms lie within this tolerance of the limit.

One immediate consequence of this definition which is frequently used is as follows.

PROPOSITION 2.5.1 $x_n \to l$ as $n \to \infty$ if and only if $x_n - l \to 0$ (as $n \to \infty$).

Example 2.5.1

If $x_n = (n + 1)/n$, then $x_n \to 1$ as $n \to \infty$.

Let $h > 0$ be given. Now, in order to establish this convergence, we must find N such that $|x_n - 1| < h$ for all $n > N$. Here

$$|x_n - 1| = \left| \frac{(n + 1)}{n} - 1 \right|$$

$$= \frac{1}{n}$$

and this is less than h if $n > 1/h$. Thus choosing $N \geqslant 1/h$, we see that, if $n > N$ then $1/n < 1/N \leqslant h$; that is, given an *arbitrary* $h > 0$, we have found N such that $|x_n - 1| < h$ for all $n > N$ as required. It should also be apparent that we proved here that $1/n \to 0$ as $n \to \infty$ as well.

Other important examples of infinite sequences are the following.

(a) $x_n = 1$ for all n,   that is, $1, 1, 1, \ldots$.

(b) $a_n = n$ for all n,   that is, $1, 2, 3, \ldots$.

(c) $y_n = (-1)^n$ for all n,   that is, $-1, 1, -1, \ldots$.

(d) $u_n = x^{n-1}$ for all n,   that is, $1, x, x^2, \ldots$.

(e) $b_n = n^\alpha$ for all n,   that is, $1, 2^\alpha, 3^\alpha, \ldots$.

(f) $v_n = \dfrac{(-1)^{n-1}}{n}$ for all n,   that is, $1, -\frac{1}{2}, \frac{1}{3}, \ldots$.

(g) $z_n = \begin{cases} 1 & \text{for } n \text{ odd,} \\ 0 & \text{for } n \text{ even,} \end{cases}$ that is, $1, 0, 1, 0, \ldots$.

Which converge?

In (a), $x_n \to 1$ is obvious. In (f), $v_n \to 0$ just as for $1/n$ since the definition uses the absolute value $|v_n|$. In (c) and (g), the sequences (y_n) and (z_n) clearly continue to oscillate without settling down. In (b), $a_n = n$ continues to grow without bound. These (and any other) sequences which do not converge are said to **diverge**.

Before discussing the convergence or divergence of (d) and (e) in detail, we need further definitions.

DEFINITIONS 2.5.2

(a) The sequence (x_n) *tends to infinity* if, given any $K > 0$, there exists N such that $x_n > K$ for all $n > N$; we write $x_n \to \infty$ as $n \to \infty$.

Similarly, $x_n \to -\infty$ as $n \to \infty$ if, for every $K' < 0$, there exists N such that $x_0 < K'$ for all $n > N$.

(b) The sequence (x_n) is *bounded* if there is a number M such that $|x_n| \leqslant M$ for all n; equivalently, x_n is bounded if there are numbers k and K such that $k \leqslant x_n \leqslant K$ for all n.

PROPOSITION 2.5.2   Any convergent sequence is bounded.

Proof   Suppose that $a_n \to a$ as $n \to \infty$. For *any* $h > 0$, there exists N such that $|a_n - a| < h$ whenever $n > N$. Thus, in particular, there exists N such that $|a_n - a| < 1$ whenever $n > N$. Then, if $n > N$,

$$|a_n| = |a_n - a + a|$$

$$\leqslant |a_n - a| + |a| < |a| + 1$$

$$= A_1$$

say. Now let $A_2 = \max\{|a_1|, |a_2|, \ldots, |a_N|\}$; then it follows that, for every n,

$$|a_n| \leqslant \max(A_1, A_2)$$

$$= M,$$

say. This completes the proof.

Of course such a bound is not unique since $|a_n| \leqslant M + 1$ as well.

Returning to our examples, we can now show the following.

PROPOSITION 2.5.3

(a) $x^n \to 0$ as $n \to \infty$ if $|x| < 1$.

(b) $x^n \to \infty$ as $n \to \infty$ if $x > 1$.

Proof

(a) There are many ways of establishing this result. One of these is included in the exercises and so this part is left for the reader.
(b) Let $x = 1 + \delta$. Then, by the binomial theorem,

$$x^n = (1 + \delta)^n$$

$$= 1 + n\delta + \frac{n(n-1)\delta^2}{2} + \ldots + \delta^n$$

$$> 1 + n\delta.$$

So, given $K > 0$, choosing $N \geqslant K/\delta$ implies that, for $n > N$,

$$x^n > 1 + n\delta$$

$$\geqslant 1 + K$$

$$> K,$$

which completes the proof.

For $x = 1$, $x^n = 1 \to 1$ as $n \to \infty$. For $x = -1$, the sequence (x^n) oscillates finitely and, for $x < -1$, it oscillates infinitely.

For the sequence (n^α) we shall prove later that, if $\alpha > 0$, then $n^\alpha \to \infty$ as $n \to \infty$, if $\alpha = 0$, then $n^\alpha = 1 \to 1$ as $n \to \infty$ and, if $\alpha < 0$, then $n^\alpha \to 0$ as $n \to \infty$.

The important **properties of limits** are as follows.

(a) If $x_n \to l$ and $x_n \to m$, then $l = m$. (That is, the limit of a sequence, if it exists, is unique.)
(b) If $a_n \to a$ and c is constant then $ca_n \to ca$ as $n \to \infty$.
(c) If $a_n \to a$, $b_n \to b$, then $a_n + b_n \to a + b$ as $n \to \infty$.
(d) If $a_n \to a$, $b_n \to b$, then $a_n b_n \to ab$ as $n \to \infty$.
(e) If $a_n \to 0$ and the sequence b_n is bounded, then $a_n b_n \to 0$ as $n \to \infty$.
(f) If $a_n \to a$, $b_n \to b$ and b, $b_n \neq 0$ for all n, then $a_n/b_n \to a/b$ as $n \to \infty$.
(g) If $a_n \to 0$ and $0 \leqslant b_n \leqslant a_n$ for all n, then $b_n \to 0$ as $n \to \infty$.
(h) The **sandwich rule**: if $a_n \to a$, $b_n \to a$ and $a_n \leqslant c_n \leqslant b_n$ for all n, then $c_n \to a$.
(i) If $a_n \to a$, $b_n \to b$ and $a_n \leqslant b_n$ for all n, then $a \leqslant b$.

The proofs of several of these are left as exercises. Many use the following.

LEMMA 2.5.1 $a_n \to a$ as $n \to \infty$ if there is a constant k such that, for every $h > 0$, there exists N for which

$$|a_n - a| < kh \qquad \text{whenever } n > N.$$

Proof Suppose that the sequence (a_n) has this property. We must show that it satisfies the definition that $a_n \to a$ as $n \to \infty$. Thus, given any $h_1 > 0$, we must find N_1 such that $|a_n - a| < h_1$ whenever $n > N_1$. (The use of the subscript 1 here is just to distinguish these quantities from those in the statement of the result.) Now, for such an h_1, $h = h_1/k > 0$ and so, by hypothesis, there exists N such that, if $n > N$, then $|a_n - a| < kh$. Taking $N_1 = N$, we thus have, as required, that

$$|a_n - a| < h_1 \qquad \text{whenever } n > N_1.$$

By way of illustration, we prove properties (d), (g) and (i) above. First, property (d) states that, if $a_n \to a$, $b_n \to b$, then $a_n b_n \to ab$ as $n \to \infty$. Let $h > 0$ be given. Now we are given $a_n \to a$, $b_n \to b$, and so there exist N_1 and N_2 such that

$$|a_n - a| < h \qquad \text{whenever } n > N_1$$

and

$$|b_n - b| < h \qquad \text{whenever } n > N_2.$$

By Lemma 2.5.1, it will be enough to find N such that $|a_n b_n - ab| < kh$ whenever $n > N$. Now,

$$|a_n b_n - ab| \leqslant |a_n b_n - a_n b + a_n b - ab|$$
$$\leqslant |a_n b_n - a_n b| + |a_n b - ab|$$
$$\leqslant |a_n||b_n - b| + |b||a_n - a|.$$

Also, since the sequence a_n is convergent, it follows from Proposition 2.5.2 that this sequence is bounded. Thus there exists A such that $|a_n| \leqslant A$ for all n. Now, if $n > N_1$ and $n > N_2$ *simultaneously*—that is, if $n > \max(N_1, N_2) = N$, say—we have

$$|a_n - a| < h$$
$$|b_n - b| < h$$

which implies that, whenever $n > N$,

$$|a_n b_n - ab| \leqslant A|b_n - b| + |b||a_n - a|$$
$$< (A + |b|)h.$$

This, with $k = A + |b|$, is precisely what we needed to show.

There are two things to note about this example. Firstly, this is entirely typical of elementary analysis proofs in that, once we had written down the definitions of what was given and of what was wanted, the argument reduced to the straightforward application of already proven results. Secondly, the lemma served to simplify the argument only slightly. Without it, we would still have

$$|a_n b_n - ab| \leqslant A|b_n - b| + |b||a_n - a|$$

and then, letting $h_2 = h/2A$, $h_1 = h/2|b|$, we could apply the definition of convergence to deduce the existence of N_1 and N_2 such that

$$|a_n - a| < h_1 \qquad \text{whenever } n > N_1$$

and

$$|b_n - b| < h_2 \qquad \text{whenever } n > N_2.$$

Hence, again taking $N = \max(N_1, N_2)$, we obtain

$$|a_n b_n - ab| < Ah_2 + |b|h_1$$

$$= \frac{h}{2} + \frac{h}{2}$$

$$= h \qquad \text{whenever } n > N,$$

as required.

There is little to choose between the two approaches—use whichever you feel more comfortable with.

Let us return to the properties of limits. Property (g) states that, if $a_n \to 0$ and $0 \leqslant b_n \leqslant a_n$ for all n, then $b_n \to 0$ as $n \to \infty$. Again we write down the definitions. Let $h > 0$ be given; there exists N_1 such that $|a_n| < h$ whenever $n > N_1$ and we must find N such that $|b_n| < h$ whenever $n > N$. Also $0 \leqslant b_n \leqslant a_n$ and so $|b_n| = b_n$ and $|a_n| = a_n$. Hence, for $n > N_1$, we have $|b_n| \leqslant |a_n| < h$; that is we can take $N = N_1$ and the proof is complete.

Property (i) states that, if $a_n \to a$, $b_n \to b$ and $a_n \leqslant b_n$ for all n, then $a \leqslant b$. Suppose that this is not so; that is, suppose that $a > b$. Then, if we take $h = (a - b)/2 > 0$, it follows from the definition of convergence that there exist N_1 and N_2 such that

$$|a_n - a| < h \qquad \text{whenever } n > N_1$$

and

$$|b_n - b| < h \qquad \text{whenever } n > N_2.$$

Equivalently, we have, for $n > \max(N_1, N_2) = N$,

$$a - h < a_n < a + h$$

and

$$b - h < b_n < b + h.$$

However, $a + h = b - h$ and so it follows that $a_n < b_n$ whenever $n > N$; this provides the required contradiction.

These properties can be used to obtain information on the convergence of many other sequences, but first a word of warning. The above statements apply only to *convergent sequences*. In particular, they do not apply to the

37

situation $a_n \to \infty$ as $n \to \infty$. **Infinity is not a number**.

However, it is true that, if $a_n \to \infty$ as $n \to \infty$, then $1/a_n \to 0$ and $n \to \infty$. (The proof of this result is left as an exercise. Simply take $K = 1/h$ in the definitions.) The converse is, of course, false.

Examples 2.5.2

1
$$x_n = \frac{an^2 + bn + c}{n^2 + 1}.$$

Dividing numerator and denominator by n^2, we get
$$x_n = \frac{a + b/n + c/n^2}{1 + 1/n^2}.$$

Now $1/n \to 0$; so, by property (b), $b/n \to 0$ while property (d) or (g) implies that $1/n^2 \to 0$. Therefore, using property (c), $a + b/n + c/n^2 \to a$ and $1 + 1/n^2 \to 1$ as $n \to \infty$ and then, since neither 1 nor $1 + 1/n^2$ is zero, we can use property (f) to deduce that $x_n \to a$ as $n \to \infty$.

Similarly, we obtain
$$\frac{3n^2 + 2n + 1}{2n^2 - 3n + 2} \to \frac{3}{2},$$

$$\frac{np + 1}{nq + 1} \to \frac{p}{q}$$

and
$$\frac{n + 1}{n^2 + 1} \to 0.$$

2 $x_n = n^\alpha$, $\alpha > 0$.

Here, since $\alpha > 0$, we see that the terms of the sequence x_n continue to grow since
$$x_{n+1} = (n + 1)^\alpha$$
$$> n^\alpha$$
$$= x_n,$$

and this growth is unbounded. Thus, we anticipate that $x_n \to \infty$ as $n \to \infty$. To prove this, let $K > 0$ be given. Then choosing $N \geqslant K^{1/\alpha}$ gives us, for $n > N$,
$$x_n = n^\alpha$$
$$> N^\alpha$$
$$\geqslant K,$$

which completes the proof.

Since $n^{-\alpha} = 1/n^{\alpha}$, it now follows that, if $\alpha < 0$, then $n^{\alpha} \to 0$ as $n \to \infty$.

In the last example, we used the fact that the terms of the sequence were growing continually so that we needed to find just one term $x_N \geqslant K$ to show that $x_n \geqslant K$ whenever $n > N$. This principle is very powerful. First, we need the following definition.

DEFINITION 2.5.3   A set S of real numbers is said to be **bounded above** if there exists a number M such that

$$x \leqslant M \qquad \text{for all } x \in S,$$

and that it is said to be **bounded below** if there exists a number m such that

$$x \geqslant m \qquad \text{for all } x \in S.$$

Such a number M is called an **upper bound** for S. Similarly, m is a **lower bound**. The set S is said to be **bounded** if it is bounded both above and below.

Now the **axiom of completeness** for the real numbers says that, if S is bounded above, then there exists a number, denoted by $\sup S$, which is the smallest number that is an upper bound for S. It is called the **least upper bound** or **supremum** of S. Thus, if S is bounded above,

(a) $\sup S$ is an upper bound of S (that is, $x \leqslant \sup S$ for all $x \in S$) and
(b)   if M is an upper bound of S, then $M \geqslant \sup S$, or, equivalently,
(b)' if $y < \sup S$ then y is not an upper bound for S (that is, there exists $x \in S$ such that $x > y$), which, in turn, is equivalent (taking $y = \sup S - h$) to
(b)" for every $h > 0$ there exists $x \in S$ such that $x > \sup S - h$.

Similar statements apply to lower bounds. A set which is bounded below has a **greatest lower bound** or **infimum**, denoted by $\inf S$.

DEFINITION 2.5.4   The sequence (a_n) is **increasing** if

$$a_1 \leqslant a_2 \leqslant a_3 \leqslant \ldots .$$

That is,

$$a_n \leqslant a_{n+1} \qquad \text{for all } n.$$

It is **strictly increasing** if $a_n < a_{n+1}$ for all n. Similarly, the sequence (a_n) is **decreasing** if $a_n \geqslant a_{n+1}$ for all n. A sequence is said to be **monotone** if it is either increasing or decreasing.

Examples 2.5.3

1 $a_n = \dfrac{n}{n^2 + 1}$.

Here,

$$a_{n+1} - a_n = \frac{n+1}{(n+1)^2 + 1} - \frac{n}{n^2 + 1}$$

$$= \frac{(n^2 + 1)(n + 1) - n(n^2 + 2n + 2)}{[(n+1)^2 + 1](n^2 + 1)}$$

$$= \frac{1 - n - n^2}{(n^2 + 1)(n^2 + 2n + 2)}$$

$$< 0 \qquad \text{for all } n.$$

Thus the sequence (a_n) is (monotone) decreasing.

2 $b_n = \dfrac{n^2 + 1}{n}$.

This is the reciprocal of the a_n in **1**. Since $0 < a_{n+1} < a_n$ for all n, it follows that $b_{n+1} > b_n$ for all n; that is, the sequence (b_n) is (strictly) increasing.

3 $a_n = 1$.

The sequence (a_n) is both increasing and decreasing—but neither strictly.

4 $x_n = n + (-1)^n$.

Here, $x_1 = 0$, $x_2 = 3$ and $x_3 = 2$. Hence, $x_1 < x_2$ and $x_2 > x_3$ and so the sequence (x_n) is neither increasing nor decreasing; it is not monotone.

PROPOSITION 2.5.5   An increasing sequence is either convergent or tends to infinity.

Proof   Suppose that the sequence (a_n) is increasing. Either the sequence (a_n) is bounded above or it is not.

(a) If the sequence (a_n) is not bounded above then, given any number $K > 0$, K is not an upper bound for the sequence (a_n). Thus, there exists a member a_N, say, of this sequence such that $a_N > K$. Since the sequence (a_n) is increasing, $a_n > K$ whenever $n > N$. By definition, therefore, $a_n \to \infty$ as $n \to \infty$.

(b) Let A be an upper bound for the sequence (a_n). Since the set $\{a_n : n = 1, 2, \ldots\}$ is bounded above, it has a least upper bound a, say. We shall now prove that $a_n \to a$ as $n \to \infty$.

Let $h > 0$ be given. We must find N such that $|a_n - a| < h$ whenever $n > N$. Firstly, since a is an upper bound, $a_n \leqslant a$ for all n and so $|a_n - a| = a - a_n$. Thus, $|a_n - a| < h$ whenever $n > N$ is equivalent to $a - a_n < h$ or

$$a_n > a - h \qquad \text{whenever } n > N.$$

Since $a - h$ is not an upper bound, it follows that there exists a_N, say, such that $a_N > a - h$. Finally, since the sequence a_n is increasing, $a_n > a_N > a - h$ whenever $n > N$ as required.

Similarly, a decreasing sequence tends to a limit or to $-\infty$. Combining these results we have the following theorem.

THEOREM 2.5.1 A bounded monotone sequence is convergent. (If it is decreasing, then the limit is the greatest lower bound whereas, if it is increasing, the limit is the least upper bound.)

The final example of this section deals with the convergence of an important sequence.

Example 2.5.4

$a_n = n^\alpha x^n \to 0$ as $n \to \infty$ for $|x| < 1$ and for all α.

Firstly, if $\alpha \leqslant 0$, then the sequence (n^α) is convergent and $x^n \to 0$; so it follows that $a_n \to 0$ as $n \to \infty$.

Suppose now that $\alpha > 0$. It is enough to consider $x > 0$ since $|a_n| = n^\alpha |x|^n$. Also, for a sequence (s_n) if $s_{n+1}/s_n \to l$ and $0 < l < 1$, then $s_n \to 0$ as $n \to \infty$.

Proof We may suppose that $s_n > 0$. Let $h = (1 - l)/2$ so that $l + h < 1$. Now, there exists N such that $|s_{n+1}/s_n - l| < h$ whenever $n > N$ and hence

$$0 < \frac{s_{n+1}}{s_n} < l + h < 1 \qquad \text{whenever } n > N,$$

which implies that the sequence s_n is decreasing—at least after N—and so convergent to its greatest lower bound, c say. Also $c \geqslant 0$. If now $c > 0$, then $s_n \to c$ and, of course, $s_{n+1} \to c$ from which it follows that $s_{n+1}/s_n \to c/c = 1$. This contradiction completes the proof.

In order to use this result, we show that

$$\left(1 + \frac{1}{n}\right)^\alpha \to 1 \qquad \text{as } n \to \infty.$$

Note that $(1 + 1/n)^\alpha$ is decreasing since $1 + 1/n$ is decreasing and positive and $\alpha > 0$. It is bounded below by 1. Hence the sequence $(1 + 1/n)^{\alpha}$ converges to its greatest lower bound. Suppose that this is not 1; that is, suppose that, for some $h > 0$

$$\left(1 + \frac{1}{n}\right)^{\alpha} > 1 + h \qquad \text{for all } n.$$

Then it follows that $1 + 1/n > (1 + h)^{1/\alpha} > 1$ for all n. However, we know that $1 + 1/n \to 1$ and so again we have a contradiction.

Combining all these parts of the proof, we get

$$\frac{a_{n+1}}{a_n} = \frac{(n+1)^{\alpha} x^{n+1}}{n^{\alpha} x^n}$$

$$= \left(1 + \frac{1}{n}\right)^{\alpha} x \to x \qquad \text{as } n \to \infty$$

from which it follows, since $0 < x < 1$, that $a_n \to 0$ as $n \to \infty$.

EXERCISES 2.5

1 Find natural numbers N_1 and N_2 such that

(a) $(\frac{9}{10})^n < 0.01$ whenever $n > N_1$ and
(b) $(\frac{9}{10})^n < 0.0001$ whenever $n > N_2$.

2 Prove that $x^n \to 0$ as $n \to \infty$ if $0 < x < 1$. (First show that this sequence is decreasing and bounded below. It therefore converges to its greatest lower bound; denote this by a and show that a/x must also be a lower bound. Deduce that $a = 0$ from which the result follows.)

3 Prove the following basic properties of limits.

(a) If $a_n \to a$ and c is constant, then $c a_n \to c a$ as $n \to \infty$.
(b) If $a_n \to a$, $b_n \to b$, then $a_n + b_n \to a + b$ as $n \to \infty$.
(c) If $a_n \to 0$ and the sequence b_n is bounded, then $a_n b_n \to 0$ as $n \to \infty$.

4 Let the sequence (a_n) be increasing and the sequence (b_n) be decreasing and suppose that $a_n \leqslant b_n$ for all n. Prove that both sequences are convergent and that $\lim a_n \leqslant \lim b_n$. (Use the fact that bounded monotone sequences are convergent.)

5 Prove the **sandwich rule**, namely that, if $a_n \to a$ and $b_n \to a$ as $n \to \infty$ and $a_n \leqslant c_n \leqslant b_n$ for all n, then $c_n \to a$ as $n \to \infty$.

6 Prove that the method of bisection converges to a solution of the equation

$f(x) = 0$. (Denote the two sequences of end-points of the interval by a_n and b_n and the sequence of the midpoints by c_n. Show that the conditions of Exercises 2.5, 4 are satisfied and therefore that $a_n \to a$ and $b_n \to b$, say. Next show that $b_n - a_n \to 0$ and therefore that $a = b$. Using the sandwich rule, it now follows that $c_n \to a$ as $n \to \infty$ as well. Also $f(a_n)f(b_n) < 0$ for all n by the design of the algorithm and, since the function f was assumed continuous, we also have that $f(a_n) \to f(a)$. We can now deduce fairly quickly that $f(c) = 0$ which will complete the proof.)

2.6 CONVERGENCE OF ITERATIVE SEQUENCES

In this section, we use the more abstract results of the last section to establish the rigorous background for the iterative methods discussed earlier. We begin with the result mentioned in section 2.3.

THEOREM 2.5.1   Suppose that the function g is continuous and differentiable on the interval $[a, b]$ and that

(a) $g([a, b]) \subseteq [a, b]$ (that is $g(x) \in [a, b]$ for all $x \in [a, b]$) and
(b) $|g'(x)| \leqslant K < 1$ for all $x \in [a, b]$.

Then the equation $x = g(x)$ has a unique solution in the interval $[a, b]$ and the sequence x_n defined for $x_0 \in [a, b]$ by

$$x_{n+1} = g(x_n) \qquad n = 0, 1, 2, \ldots$$

converges to this solution.

Proof   Firstly, consider the function $f: [a, b] \to R$ given by

$$f(x) = x - g(x).$$

Since $g(a) \in [a, b]$, it follows that

$$f(a) = a - g(a) \leqslant 0$$

and similarly, $f(b) \geqslant 0$. Now f is continuous and so there exists $s \in [a, b]$ such that $f(s) = 0$; that is, $s = g(s)$. The fact that s is the only solution of this equation in $[a, b]$ follows from the mean-value theorem. Suppose that $t = g(t)$, where $t \in [a, b]$; then $g(t) - g(s) = (t - s)g'(\theta)$ for some value θ between s and t. However, $g(t) - g(s) = t - s$ and so this implies that

$$t - s = (t - s)g'(\theta).$$

Since, by Theorem 2.6.1(b), $|g'(\theta)| < 1$, this can only be true if $t = s$. Thus the solution is unique.

We make further use of the mean-value theorem in order to establish the

43

convergence. Since $x_0 \in [a, b]$, Theorem 2.6.1(a) implies that $x_n \in [a, b]$ for every n. We denote by e_n the error in the iterate x_n so that

$$e_n = x_n - s.$$

Then we have

$$|e_{n+1}| = |g(x_n) - g(s)|$$
$$= |x_n - s| |g'(\alpha_n)|,$$

where α_n lies between x_n and s—and therefore in $[a, b]$. It now follows that $|g'(\alpha_n)| < 1$ and hence that

$$|e_{n+1}| \leqslant K |e_n|,$$

which in turn implies that

$$|e_{n+1}| \leqslant K^{n+1} |e_0|.$$

Since $K < 1$, we can now deduce that $e_n \to 0$ and therefore that $x_n \to s$ as $n \to \infty$, as required.

The importance of this and other results on the convergence of iterative schemes is that we can use such a theorem to decide *in advance* whether a particular iteration will work. If $|g'(x)| < 1$ for all x near the solution and the initial guess x_0 is 'close enough' to the solution, then the iteration $x_{n+1} = g(x_n)$ will converge to it.

Example 2.6.1

Show that the equation

$$x^3 - x^2 - x - 1 = 0$$

has a solution in $[1.6, 2.1]$. Decide which of the following iterations will converge to this solution and use it to obtain the solution to three decimal places.

(a) $x_{n+1} = x_n^3 - x_n^2 - 1$

(b) $x_{n+1} = \left(\dfrac{x_n + 1}{x_n - 1} \right)^{1/2}$

(c) $x_{n+1} = 1 + \dfrac{1}{x_n} + \dfrac{1}{x_n^2}$.

Firstly, with $f(x) = x^3 - x^2 - x - 1$,

$$f(1.6) = -1.064$$

and

$$f(2.1) = 1.751.$$

Since f is continuous, there is a solution of $f(x) = 0$ in $[1.6, 2.1]$.

For (a),

$$g(x) = x^3 - x^2 - 1.$$

Here

$$g(1.6) = 0.536$$

which is outside $[1.6, 2.1]$. Thus condition Theorem 2.6.1(a) fails—g does not map the interval onto itself.

For (b),

$$g(x) = \left(\frac{x+1}{x-1}\right)^{1/2}.$$

This time

$$g(1.6) \approx 2.082 \in [1.6, 2.1]$$

and

$$g(2.1) \approx 1.679 \in [1.6, 2.1].$$

Also g is decreasing for $x > 1$ and so it follows that $g([1.6, 2.1]) \subseteq [1.6, 2.1]$. Thus Theorem 2.6.1(a) is satisfied. Next,

$$g'(x) = -(x+1)^{-1/2}(x-1)^{-3/2}$$

and so

$$|g'(1.6)| \approx 1.334$$

$$> 1$$

which implies that Theorem 2.6.1(b) fails.

For (c),

$$g(x) = 1 + \frac{1}{x} + \frac{1}{x^2}$$

is decreasing for $x > 0$;

$$g(1.6) \approx 2.016$$

and

$$g(2.1) \approx 1.703$$

so that $g([1.6, 2.1]) \subseteq [1.6, 2.1]$; that is, Theorem 2.6.1(a) is satisfied. Here,

$$g'(x) = \frac{1}{x^2} - \frac{2}{x^3}$$

45

so that

$$|g'(x)| = \frac{1}{x^2} + \frac{2}{x^3}$$

which is again decreasing as x increases. Since

$$|g'(1.6)| \approx 0.879$$

$$< 1,$$

it follows that Theorem 2.6.1(b) is satisfied also. Thus iteration (c) will converge.

Choose x_0 to be the midpoint of the interval; $x_0 = 1.85$. Then

$$x_1 = 1.832\,725,$$

$$x_2 = 1.843\,354,$$

$$x_3 = 1.836\,784,$$

$$x_4 = 1.840\,834,$$

$$x_5 = 1.838\,333,$$

$$x_6 = 1.839\,875,$$

$$x_7 = 1.838\,924,$$

$$x_8 = 1.839\,511,$$

$$x_9 = 1.839\,149,$$

$$x_{10} = 1.839\,372.$$

At this point we see that $x_9 = x_{10} = 1.839$ to three decimal places, which suggests this is the required solution. Our analysis does *not* allow us to state this with certainty. In fact, since, in this case, $g'(x) < 0$ for all $x \in [1.6, 2.1]$, if we look back to the iteration diagrams (Fig. 2.1), we see that each pair of iterates brackets the solution s. Thus we may conclude that $1.839\,149 < s < 1.839\,372$ and therefore that $s = 1.839$ to three decimal places.

In our earlier discussion of iteration, we saw from the Taylor series expansion of g about s that

$$x_{n+1} - s = (x_n - s)g'(s) + \frac{(x_n - s)^2 g''(s)}{2} + \dots$$

or, in the notation introduced above,

$$e_{n+1} = e_n g'(s) + \frac{e_n^2 g''(s)}{2} + \dots . \tag{2.16}$$

Now, if we can design our iteration function g so that $g'(s) = 0$, this yields, when the terms in e_n^3 and higher powers are neglected,

$$e_{n+1} \approx \frac{e_n^2 g''(s)}{2}.$$

This would mean that the error tends to zero much faster. For example, suppose that $g''(s) = 2$ and that $e_0 \approx 0.1$. Then $e_1 \approx 0.01$, $e_2 \approx 0.0001$, $e_3 \approx 0.00000001$, that is, the number of decimal places which are accurate in the solution approximately doubles with every iteration.

Contrast this with the last example where we had $e_0 \approx 0.01$ and yet had accuracy to only three decimal places after 10 iterations.

How can we achieve this so-called **quadratic convergence**?

We seek an iteration function g such that

$$f(x) = 0 \Leftrightarrow x = g(x)$$

and $g'(s) = 0$ where s is the required solution. The simplest function g satisfying the first condition is defined by $g(x) = x + f(x)$ or, slightly more generally, by

$$g(x) = x + cf(x) \qquad c \neq 0. \qquad (2.17)$$

In this case,

$$g'(x) = 1 + cf'(x)$$

and so $g'(s) = 0$ for $c = -1/f'(s)$ but, of course, we do not know s and so cannot obtain the appropriate constant c.

A further generalisation is to take

$$g(x) = x + c(x)f(x) \qquad (2.18)$$

where $c(x) \neq 0$. Then

$$g'(x) = 1 + c'(x)f(x) + c(x)f'(x) \qquad (2.19)$$

and, since $f(s) = 0$,

$$g'(s) = 1 + c(s)f'(s). \qquad (2.20)$$

To force $g'(s) = 0$, we thus require $c(s) = -1/f'(s)$ which can obviously be achieved by choosing $c(x) = -1/f'(x)$. The resulting iteration is

$$x_{n+1} = g(x_n) = x_n - \frac{f(x_n)}{f'(x_n)}; \qquad (2.21)$$

that is, we have rediscovered Newton's method.

Since this has been constructed so that $g'(s) = 0$, it follows that $|g'(x)| < 1$ near the solution and therefore that this iteration will converge (and quickly) for x_0 sufficiently close to s. The one danger here is the situation where $f'(x)$ becomes small near the solution in which case this formula is likely to be unstable. In particular, Newton's method requires modification if a 'double root' is to be found.

Examples 2.6.2

1 Find the solution of

$$x^3 - x^2 - x - 1 = 0$$

near $x = 2$ using Newton's method. Here,

$$f(x) = x^3 - x^2 - x - 1$$

and

$$f'(x) = 3x^2 - 2x - 1.$$

Hence

$$g(x) = x - \frac{f(x)}{f'(x)}$$

$$= \frac{x(3x^2 - 2x - 1) - (x^3 - x^2 - x - 1)}{3x^2 - 2x - 1}$$

$$= \frac{2x^3 - x^2 + 1}{3x^2 - 2x - 1}.$$

Choosing $x_0 = 2$, we get

$$x_1 = \tfrac{13}{7}$$

$$= 1.857\,142\,9,$$

$$x_2 = 1.839\,544\,5,$$

$$x_3 = 1.839\,286\,8,$$

$$x_4 = 1.839\,286\,8,$$

that is, accuracy to seven decimal places in just four iterations.

2 Consider the example used earlier of finding square roots by Newton's method. The iteration for solving $x^2 = c$ is

$$x_{n+1} = \frac{x_n + c/x_n}{2}.$$

Now to study the convergence of this, we consider

$$x_{n+1} - \sqrt{c} = \frac{x_n^2 - 2x_n\sqrt{c} + c}{2x_n}$$

$$= \frac{(x_n - \sqrt{c})^2}{2x_n}.$$

Similarly, $x_{n+1} + \sqrt{c} = (x_n + \sqrt{c})^2/2x_n$ and so we find that

$$\frac{x_{n+1} - \sqrt{c}}{x_{n+1} + \sqrt{c}} = \left(\frac{x_n - \sqrt{c}}{x_n + \sqrt{c}}\right)^2$$

$$= \left(\frac{x_{n-1} - \sqrt{c}}{x_{n-1} + \sqrt{c}}\right)^4$$

$$= \ldots$$

$$= \left(\frac{x_0 - \sqrt{c}}{x_0 + \sqrt{c}}\right)^{2^{n+1}}.$$

For any $x_0 > 0$, we have $|(x_0 - \sqrt{c})/(x_0 + \sqrt{c})| < 1$ and so it follows that $(x_{n+1} - \sqrt{c})/(x_{n+1} + \sqrt{c}) \to 0$ as $n \to \infty$. Therefore $x_n \to \sqrt{c}$ for every choice $x_0 > 0$. Furthermore, from the above analysis, it follows that $x_n > \sqrt{c}$ for $n \geqslant 1$ and, of course, that $x_n > x_{n+1}$. Hence we deduce that

$$e_{n+1} = x_{n+1} - \sqrt{c}$$

$$= \frac{e_n^2(x_{n+1} + \sqrt{c})}{(x_n + \sqrt{c})^2}$$

$$\leqslant \frac{e_n^2}{x_n + \sqrt{c}}$$

$$\leqslant \frac{e_n^2}{2\sqrt{c}}.$$

Thus, for example with $c = 25$ and $x_0 = 5.1$, we have $e_0 = 0.1$, $e_1 \leqslant 0.001$, $e_2 \leqslant 10^{-7}$, $e_3 \leqslant 10^{-15}$, ... In particular, just two iterations are needed for standard single-precision floating-point accuracy which is approximately equivalent to seven significant figures. These first two iterations produce

$$x_1 = 5.000\,980\,4,$$

$$x_2 = 5.000\,000\,1,$$

and the second of these indeed has the claimed precision.

EXERCISES 2.6

1 Show that, if the iteration function g satisfies $|g'(s)| < 1$, then there exists h such that, if $|s - x_0| < h$, then the iteration $x_{n+1} = g(x_n)$ will converge to the solution s.

2 Consider Newton's method for finding reciprocals which we discussed in Exercise 2.3, **3**. This gave rise to the iteration $x_{n+1} = x_n(2 - cx_n)$ which satisfies $|g'(x)| < 1$ for all $x \in (1/2c, 3/2c)$. Prove that

$$x_{n+1} - \frac{1}{c} = -c\left(x_n - \frac{1}{c}\right)^2,$$

from which it follows that $x_{n+1} < 1/c$ for all n. Prove too that, if $x_n < 1/c$, then $x_{n+1} > x_n$. We now have $x_1 < x_2 < x_3 < \dots < 1/c$ and hence that the sequence x_n is convergent. Deduce that $x_n \to 1/c$ as $n \to \infty$.

Show that for the special case of finding the reciprocal of a normalised floating-point number where $c = 2f \in [1, 2)$ then taking $x_0 = \frac{3}{4}$ means that five iterations are sufficient to obtain an error of at most 2^{-33}. (This is greater precision that is required for any standard single-length floating-point representation.)

3 Prove that the iterative schemes used in Exercises 2.3, **1** and **2**, do indeed converge from the starting points chosen.

4 Prove that, if the iteration function g satisfies $g(x) \in [a, b]$ and $-1 < g'(x) < 0$ for all $x \in [a, b]$, then, if $x_0 < s$, we have

$$x_0 < x_2 < \dots < s < \dots < x_3 < x_1$$

so that each pair of successive iterates brackets the solution.

3 SERIES APPROXIMATION OF FUNCTIONS; CONVERGENCE OF SERIES

3.1 INTRODUCTION

Frequently within mathematics, and especially in computation, we are obliged to use approximations to functions (and other functional quantities such as integrals and derivatives) because their *exact* values *cannot* be calculated.

All the function buttons on your calculator–even the arithmetic ones— obtain approximate evaluations of the functions. Similarly, standard library functions such as EXP, LOG, COS and ATN on the computer are evaluated by sophisticated approximation schemes which are often based on the use of a power series. The details of how these operations are performed are, unfortunately, outside the scope of this course although, in the next chapter, we shall consider briefly the method of approximation used in most hand-calculators.

We wish to approximate the value $f(x)$ in such a way that any specified accuracy can be achieved. One of the simplest approaches (in principle, at least) is to use a polynomial approximation derived from a Taylor series expansion of f about a convenient point.

Suppose then that f has the Taylor series expansion

$$f(a) + (x-a)f'(a) + \frac{1}{2!}(x-a)^2 f''(a) + \ldots = \sum_{r=0}^{\infty} \frac{(x-a)^r f^{(r)}(a)}{r!}, \quad (3.1)$$

where we have used the convention that $0! = 1$. Then, for x near a (so that $|x-a|$ is small), we could use the finite series

$$\sum_{r=0}^{n} \frac{(x-a)^r f^{(r)}(a)}{r!} = f(a) + (x-a)f'(a) + \ldots + \frac{(x-a)^n f^{(n)}(a)}{n!} \quad (3.2)$$

as an approximation to $f(x)$. Denote this finite sum by $f_n(x)$. For this approximation to be of any real value, we must have $f_n(x) \to f(x)$ as $n \to \infty$.

It will then follow that, for any required tolerance h, there exists N such that

$$|f_n(x) - f(x)| < h \qquad \text{whenever } n \geqslant N$$

and therefore that $f_N(x)$ would be a suitable approximation.

Obviously we do not wish to do more work than necessary! Thus, in this situation, we seek the smallest N for which the condition is satisfied. Note that this is equivalent to

$$\left| \sum_{r=N+1}^{\infty} \frac{(x-a)^r f^{(r)}(a)}{r!} \right| < h,$$

and so we must consider the whole tail of the series and not just the next term.

The sequence which we denoted by $(f_n(x))$ here is known as the **sequence of partial sums** of the **infinite series** and the question at issue is the **convergence** of this series to the correct **sum** $f(x)$. The convergence of series is the theme of the next few sections of this chapter.

Before discussing such topics in detail, it is worth observing that most of the basic elementary functions are either defined by, or derived from, series:

$$\exp x = 1 + x + \frac{x^2}{2!} + \dots$$

$$= \sum_{r=0}^{\infty} \frac{x^r}{r!}$$

$$\cos x = 1 - \frac{x^2}{2!} + \frac{x^4}{4!} + \dots$$

$$= \sum_{r=0}^{\infty} \frac{(-1)^r x^{2r}}{(2r)!}$$

$$\sin x = x - \frac{x^3}{3!} + \frac{x^5}{5!} + \dots$$

$$= \sum_{r=0}^{\infty} \frac{(-1)^r x^{2r+1}}{(2r+1)!}$$

are the fundamental definitions. From these, we obtain the other trigonometric functions such as tan and sec and the hyperbolic functions

$$\cosh x = \frac{\exp x + \exp(-x)}{2}$$

and

$$\sinh x = \frac{\exp x - \exp(-x)}{2}.$$

From elementary calculus, we know that

$$\frac{d}{dx}[\ln(1+x)] = \frac{1}{1+x}$$

$$\frac{d}{dx}(\tan^{-1} x) = \frac{1}{1+x^2}$$

$$\frac{d}{dx}(\tanh^{-1} x) = \frac{1}{1-x^2}.$$

We shall see later that this enables us to derive series expansions for these functions from the **geometric series**

$$1 + x + x^2 + \ldots = \sum_{r=0}^{\infty} x^r$$

which has the sum $1/(1-x)$ provided that $|x| < 1$.

3.2 CONVERGENCE OF SERIES

In this section, we make the ideas discussed in the introduction precise and consider some of the basic properties and fundamental examples of infinite series.

DEFINITION 3.1   Consider the infinite series

$$a_1 + a_2 + a_3 + \ldots = \sum_{r=1}^{\infty} a_r$$

and denote by (s_n) the sequence of **partial sums** given by

$$s_n = a_1 + a_2 + a_3 + \ldots + a_n$$

$$= \sum_{r=1}^{n} a_r.$$

The series $\sum_{r=1}^{\infty} a_r$ **converges** to the **sum** s if $s_n \to s$ as $n \to \infty$. A series which does not converge is said to **diverge**.

Examples 3.2.1

1 The **geometric series** is

$$\sum_{r=0}^{\infty} x^r = 1 + x + x^2 + \ldots.$$

Here,

$$s_{n-1} = 1 + x + x^2 + \ldots + x^{n-1}$$

and so

$$xs_{n-1} = x + x^2 + \ldots + x^{n-1} + x^n$$

from which we deduce that $(1-x)s_{n-1} = 1 - x^n$ or

$$s_{n-1} = \frac{1 - x^n}{1 - x} \qquad \text{provided that } x \neq 1. \tag{3.3}$$

If $|x| < 1$, then we already know that $x^n \to 0$ as $n \to \infty$ and so it follows that $s_{n-1} \to 1/(1-x)$ as $n \to \infty$; that is, for $|x| < 1$,

$$\sum_{r=0}^{\infty} x^r = \frac{1}{1 - x}. \tag{3.4}$$

For $x \geq 1$,

$$s_n = 1 + x + x^2 + \ldots + x^n$$

$$\geq n + 1 \to \infty \qquad \text{as } n \to \infty.$$

For $x = -1$,

$$s_n = 1 - 1 + 1 - \ldots + (-1)^n$$

$$= \begin{cases} 1 & \text{if } n \text{ is even,} \\ 0 & \text{if } n \text{ is odd,} \end{cases}$$

which does not converge. For $x < -1$, s_n oscillates infinitely. Thus, the geometric series converges for $|x| < 1$ and diverges for $|x| \geq 1$. We shall make frequent reference to this result.

2

$$\sum_{r=1}^{\infty} \frac{1}{r(r+1)}$$

converges. Here

$$a_r = \frac{1}{r(r+1)}$$

$$= \frac{1}{r} - \frac{1}{r+1}$$

and so

$$s_n = a_1 + a_2 + \ldots + a_n$$

$$= \left(1 - \frac{1}{2}\right) + \left(\frac{1}{2} - \frac{1}{3}\right) + \ldots + \left(\frac{1}{n} - \frac{1}{n+1}\right)$$

$$= 1 - \frac{1}{n+1}.$$

Therefore,

$$s_n \to 1 \qquad \text{as } n \to \infty$$

or

$$\sum_{r=1}^{\infty} \frac{1}{r(r+1)} = 1.$$

3 The **harmonic series**

$$\sum_{r=1}^{\infty} \frac{1}{r}$$

diverges. Here, the sequence s_n is increasing since every term in the series is positive. By Proposition 2.5.5 it follows that either the sequence (s_n) converges or $s_n \to \infty$ as $n \to \infty$. We show that $s_n \to \infty$ by establishing, by induction, that

$$s_{2^n} > \frac{n+1}{2} \qquad n = 1, 2, \ldots .$$

This will be sufficient to show that the sequence (s_n) is not bounded and hence is divergent.

Now $s_{2^0} = s_1 = 1 > \frac{1}{2}$ and so the result is true for $n = 0$. Suppose that, for some k, $s_{2^k} > (k+1)/2$. Then

$$s_{2^{k+1}} = 1 + \frac{1}{2} + \ldots + \frac{1}{2^k} + \frac{1}{2^k + 1} + \frac{1}{2^k + 2} + \ldots + \frac{1}{2^{k+1}}$$

$$= s_{2^k} + \frac{1}{2^k + 1} + \ldots + \frac{1}{2^{k+1}}$$

$$> \frac{k+1}{2} + \frac{2^k}{2^{k+1}}$$

$$= \frac{k+1}{2} + \frac{1}{2}$$

$$= \frac{k+2}{2}$$

and so the result follows by induction.

These three standard examples form the basis of many of the tests for convergence of series. Some of the basic properties carry over from the convergence of sequences. Thus, by considering the sequences of partial sums, we get

$$\sum_{r=1}^{\infty} a_r, \ \sum_{r=1}^{\infty} b_r \text{ convergent} \Rightarrow \sum_{r=1}^{\infty} (a_r \pm b_r) \text{ convergent}$$

and

$$\sum_{r=1}^{\infty} a_r \text{ convergent} \Rightarrow \sum_{r=1}^{\infty} ca_r \text{ convergent for any constant } c.$$

One test which can be very useful in showing that a particular series is **divergent** is the following theorem.

THEOREM 3.2.1 (the vanishing test)   If $\sum_{r=1}^{\infty} a_r$ converges then $a_n \to 0$ as $n \to \infty$.

Proof Let (s_n) be the sequence of partial sums. Then $s_n \to s$, say, and so it follows that $s_n - s_{n-1} \to 0$ as $n \to \infty$. That is,

$$a_1 + a_2 + \ldots + a_n - (a_1 + a_2 + \ldots + a_{n-1}) = a_n \to 0,$$

as required.

Note that the converse is false: $1/n \to 0$ as $n \to \infty$ but $\sum_{r=1}^{\infty} 1/r$ diverges. A further example of this follows.

Example 3.2.2

Consider $\sum_{r=1}^{\infty} a_r$ where $a_r = \sqrt{r} - \sqrt{r-1}$. Now

$$a_n = \frac{n - (n-1)}{\sqrt{n} + \sqrt{n-1}}$$

$$\leqslant \frac{1}{\sqrt{n}}$$

$$\to 0 \qquad \text{as } n \to \infty$$

but

$$s_n = a_1 + a_2 + \ldots + a_n$$

$$= (1 - 0) + (\sqrt{2} - 1) + \ldots + (\sqrt{n} - \sqrt{n-1})$$

$$= \sqrt{n} \to \infty.$$

Thus,

*Theorem 3.2.1 can **never** be used to prove convergence of a series.*

EXERCISE 3.2

1 Find the sums of the infinite series $\sum_{r=1}^{\infty} a_r$ where

(a) $a_r = \dfrac{1}{r(r+2)}$,

(b) $a_r = \dfrac{2}{(r+1)(r+2)}$,

(c) $a_r = (-\frac{1}{3})^r$,

(d) $a_r = \dfrac{1}{5^{r-1}}$,

(e) $a_r = \dfrac{1}{r(r+1)(r+2)} - \dfrac{2}{3^r}$.

3.3 SERIES OF POSITIVE TERMS

In this section, we consider several tests relating to the convergence of a series $\sum a_n$ where $a_n \geqslant 0$ for all n. (Note that we have omitted any explicit mention of the limits of the summation here.) We begin with a very simple result which will be helpful later.

LEMMA 3.3.1 A series of positive terms is either convergent or tends to infinity.

Proof Since the terms are positive, the sequence of partial sums is increasing. The result follows from Proposition 2.5.5.

We use this to prove the **comparison test**.

THEOREM 3.3.1 (the comparison test) Let $\sum u_r$, $\sum v_r$ be series of positive terms and suppose that there exists a constant c such that $u_n \leqslant c v_n$ for all n.

(a) If $\sum v_r$ is convergent, then so is $\sum u_r$.

(b) If $\sum u_r$ is divergent, then so is $\sum v_r$.

Proof Let (s_n) and (t_n) be the sequences of partial sums of $\sum u_r$ and $\sum v_r$ respectively. By Lemma 3.3.1, the sequences (s_n) and (t_n) are increasing. To prove (a) if $\sum v_r$ is convergent, then $t_n \to t$, say, and $ct_n \to ct$. Also $s_n \leqslant ct_n \leqslant ct$ for all n and so the sequence (s_n) is bounded above (and increasing) and therefore convergent. (b) can easily be proved by contradiction using (a). The proof is left to the reader as an exercise.

This is probably the most important single convergence test of all.

Examples 3.3.1

Consider the series $\sum 1/n^k$ for positive values of k.

1 $\sum 1/n^2$ is convergent.

We have already shown that $\sum 1/n(n+1) = 1$. Also for all $n \geqslant 1$, $n + 1 \leqslant 2n$ and so

$$0 < \frac{1}{n^2} \leqslant \frac{2}{n(n+1)}.$$

Hence $\sum 1/n^2$ is convergent by the comparison test.

2 $\sum 1/n^k$ is convergent for all $k \geqslant 2$.

This is now easy to prove by the comparison test using the convergence of $\sum 1/n^2$. The details are left as an exercise.

3 $\sum 1/n^k$ is divergent if $k \leqslant 1$.

With $k \leqslant 1$, we have $0 < 1/n \leqslant 1/n^k$ and the harmonic series $\sum 1/n$ is divergent. Hence $\sum 1/n^k$ is divergent for $k \leqslant 1$ by the comparison test.

4 Is $\sum 1/n^k$ convergent or divergent for $1 < k < 2$?

We cannot use the comparison test here since we have

$$\frac{1}{n^2} < \frac{1}{n^k} < \frac{1}{n}$$

so that the terms of this series are *larger* than those of the known *convergent* series $\sum 1/n^2$ and *smaller* than those of the known *divergent* series $\sum 1/n$.

However, we can use the same approach as was adopted for the harmonic series—grouping terms together in blocks of size 2^n but this time obtaining upper bounds. We can then apply Lemma 3.3.1 to establish the convergence of the series. Now

$$\frac{1}{2^k} + \frac{1}{3^k} < \frac{2}{2^k} = \frac{1}{2^{k-1}}$$

$$\frac{1}{4^k} + \frac{1}{5^k} + \frac{1}{6^k} + \frac{1}{7^k} < \frac{4}{4^k}$$

$$= \frac{1}{4^{k-1}}$$

$$= \frac{1}{2^{2(k-1)}}$$

and, in general,

$$\frac{1}{(2^n)^k} + \cdots + \frac{1}{(2^{n+1} - 1)^k} < \frac{2^n}{(2^n)^k}$$

$$= \frac{1}{2^{n(k-1)}}.$$

Therefore,

$$s_{2^{n+1}-1} < 1 + \frac{1}{2^{k-1}} + \cdots + \frac{1}{2^{n(k-1)}}$$

$$\rightarrow \frac{1}{1 - 1/2^{k-1}},$$

since the common ratio of this geometric series is $1/2^{k-1} < 1$. Since the terms of the series are positive, the sequence of partial sums is increasing and so the whole series must converge to this same sum.

Summarising, we have

$$\sum \frac{1}{n^k} \quad \begin{cases} \text{diverges for } k \leqslant 1 \\ \text{converges for } k > 1. \end{cases}$$

Since the convergence of sequences, and therefore of series, is a property of eventual behaviour the convergence of a series is not affected by changing any *finite* number of terms. Similarly, the conclusions of the comparison test are equally valid even if we only have

$$u_n \leqslant c v_n \qquad \text{whenever } n > N.$$

Example 3.3.2

$\sum 1/n!$ is convergent.

Since $1/n! < 1/n(n+1)$ for all $n \geqslant 4$ and we have already seen that $\sum 1/n(n+1)$ is convergent, the result follows by the comparison test.

The comparison test can also be used to establish the convergence of series such as $\sum 1/(1+2^n)$ or $\sum 1/(n^2-n+1)$ and the divergence of $\sum 2/(n+4)$.

The next test—the ratio test—is particularly useful when considering series where there is a multiplicative relation between successive terms. It is therefore especially valuable in examining the convergence of power series. The validity of **d'Alembert's ratio test** is proved using the comparison test and the known behaviour of geometric series.

THEOREM 3.3.2 (d'Alembert's ratio test)   Let $\sum u_r$ be a series of positive terms and suppose that $u_{n+1}/u_n \to l$ as $n \to \infty$. If $l < 1$, then $\sum u_r$ is convergent and, if $l > 1$, then $\sum u_r$ is divergent.

Proof   Firstly, suppose that $l < 1$ and let $h = (1-l)/2$. From the definition of convergence of *sequences*, it follows that there exists N such that

$$\left| \frac{u_{n+1}}{u_n} - l \right| < h \qquad \text{whenever } n > N$$

which implies, in particular, that

$$\frac{u_{n+1}}{u_n} < l + h = k, \quad \text{say,} \qquad \text{whenever } n > N.$$

By the choice of h, $k < 1$ and so, for $n > N$,

$$u_n < u_N k^{n-N} = ck^n, \quad \text{say.}$$

Since $\sum k^n$ is convergent, $\sum u_r$ is convergent by the comparison test.

For the case $l > 1$, we can obtain, in the same way, that $u_n > u_N k^{n-N}$ where now $k > 1$. Hence, $u_r \to \infty$ from which it follows that $\sum u_r$ is divergent.

Remarks

(a) If $u_{n+1}/u_n \to 1$, then the ratio test tells us nothing. For example, $u_{n+1}/u_n \to 1$ for both $u_n = 1/n$ and $u_n = 1/n^2$ but $\sum 1/n$ diverges and $\sum 1/n^2$ converges.

(b) In the proof, we obtained, for the convergent case,

$$\frac{u_{n+1}}{u_n} \leqslant k < 1 \qquad \text{whenever } n > N.$$

This condition is sufficient as it stands; we do not need to obtain the limit although the limit form is often more convenient, especially in determining the behaviour of power series.

Examples 3.3.3

1 $\sum_{r=0}^{\infty} x^r/r!$ is convergent for all $x > 0$.

Here,

$$\frac{u_{n+1}}{u_n} = \frac{x^{n+1}}{(n+1)!} \frac{n!}{x^n}$$

$$= \frac{x}{n+1}$$

$$\to 0 < 1.$$

(Of course, we shall see later that the exponential series is convergent for all values of x but the tests which we have so far developed apply only to series of positive terms.)

2 $\sum 1/n2^n$ is convergent.

Here,

$$\frac{u_{n+1}}{u_n} = \frac{n2^n}{(n+1)2^{n+1}}$$

$$= \frac{n}{2(n+1)}$$

$$\leqslant \frac{1}{2}$$

$$< 1 \qquad \text{for all } n,$$

and so, using the alternative form of the ratio test in the above remark, this series converges. (In this case, comparison with $\sum 1/2^n$ would yield the result more easily.)

3 $\sum 3^n/2^n n^2$ is divergent.

Here, we get

$$\frac{u_{n+1}}{u_n} = \frac{3n^2}{2(n+1)^2}$$

$$\to \frac{3}{2}$$

$$> 1.$$

EXERCISES 3.3

1 Test the following series for convergence.

(a) $\displaystyle\sum_{r=1}^{\infty} \frac{1}{r(r+2)}$.

(b) $\displaystyle\sum_{r=1}^{\infty} r^{-1/3}$.

(c) $\displaystyle\sum_{r=1}^{\infty} \frac{r}{(r^2+r+1)}$.

(d) $\displaystyle\sum_{r=0}^{\infty} \frac{1}{(2^r+1)}$.

(e) $\displaystyle\sum_{r=0}^{\infty} \frac{(r!)^2}{(2r)!}$.

(f) $\displaystyle\sum_{r=2}^{\infty} \frac{1}{\ln r}$.

(g) $\displaystyle\sum_{r=1}^{\infty} \frac{r^3}{2^{r/2}}$.

2 Show that, if a_n is a decreasing sequence and $\sum a_r$ is convergent, then $na_n \to 0$ as $n \to \infty$. (Hint: consider $s_{2n} - s_n$ and show that $na_{2n} \to 0$.)

3.4 SERIES OF MIXED SIGN; ABSOLUTE CONVERGENCE

So far we have only discussed the convergence of series in which all the terms have the same sign but we saw earlier that, for example,

$$\cos x = 1 - \frac{x^2}{2!} + \frac{x^4}{4!} - \dots.$$

That is, we have a series of mixed sign. In this particular case, it is of alternating sign and, for this special sign pattern, we have a special convergence test.

THEOREM 3.4.1 (the alternating-sign or alternating-series test)   Suppose that (a_n) is a decreasing sequence with limit 0 (that is, $a_n \geqslant a_{n+1}$ for all n and $a_n \to 0$ as $n \to \infty$); then the series

$$\sum_{r=0}^{\infty} (-1)^r a_r = a_0 - a_1 + a_2 - a_3 + \dots$$

is convergent.

Proof   Consider the sequence of partial sums given by

$$s_n = a_0 - a_1 + a_2 - \ldots + (-1)^n a_n.$$

Then, since the sequence (a_n) is decreasing,

$$s_{2n+1} - s_{2n-1} = (-1)^{2n} a_{2n} + (-1)^{2n+1} a_{2n+1}$$

$$= a_{2n} - a_{2n+1}$$

$$\geqslant 0$$

and, similarly,

$$s_{2n+2} - s_{2n} = a_{2n+2} - a_{2n+1}$$

$$\leqslant 0.$$

Hence the sequence (s_{2n-1}) is increasing and the sequence (s_{2n}) is decreasing. Also

$$s_{2n} - s_{2n-1} = a_{2n}$$

$$\geqslant 0$$

so that $s_{2n-1} \leqslant s_{2n}$ for all n. Using the result of Exercise 2.5, **4**, it follows that both these sequences converge and, since $s_{2n} - s_{2n-1} = a_{2n} \to 0$, their limits are the same. Therefore the sequence (s_n) converges as required.

It is worth noting here that the sum is bracketed between each successive pair of partial sums, that is,

$$s_1 \leqslant s_3 \leqslant \ldots \leqslant s \leqslant \ldots \leqslant s_2 \leqslant s_0.$$

In particular, $a_0 - a_1 \leqslant s \leqslant a_0$. This bracketing property can be very useful in the approximation of functions since it allows us to guarantee the accuracy of the value obtained.

Example 3.4.1

$$\sum_{r=1}^{\infty} \frac{(-1)^{r-1}}{r} = 1 - \tfrac{1}{2} + \tfrac{1}{3} - \tfrac{1}{4} + \ldots$$

is convergent.

Here $a_n = 1/n$ which is certainly decreasing with limit 0 and so the convergence of this alternating series follows immediately from Theorem 3.4.1. From the expansion of $\ln(1+x)$, we see that its sum is $\ln 2$.

In this case the convergence is so slow that this would not be a sensible way of evaluating $\ln 2$. From the above observation, we see that, even using 1000 terms of the series, we can only be sure that the error does not exceed $1/1001$ or about 0.001. Although this bound is slightly pessimistic, it does give a realistic idea of the merits of this approximation. Of course for a small argument x, using the series $x - x^2/2 + x^3/3 - x^4/4 + \ldots$ does provide a rapidly convergent method of approximating $\ln(1 + x)$. For example, with $x = 0.1$, the fact that alternate partial sums bracket the true sum implies that using just eight terms of the series results in an error less than $10^{-9}/9$ which is sufficient to yield standard single-length floating-point accuracy.

This is a very special sign pattern, however, and in this case it is possible to rearrange the series in a form which is often more rapidly convergent. For a formal development of **Euler's method**, it is convenient to introduce the **shift operator** E defined on a sequence (a_n) by

$$Eu_n = u_{n+1}$$

so that $E^2 a_n = a_{n+2}$ and, in general, $E^k a_n = a_{n+k}$. The **forward difference operator** Δ (which we shall meet again in the next chapter) is defined by

$$\Delta a_n = a_{n+1} - a_n$$

and then higher-order differences are defined by $\Delta^{k+1} a_n = \Delta^k a_{n+1} - \Delta^k a_n$ for $k = 1, 2, \ldots$. Note that $E a_n - a_n = \Delta a_n$ and so (since these operators are linear) we may write

$$E = 1 + \Delta.$$

Formally, for the alternating series $\sum (-1)^r a_r$, we can write

$$
\begin{aligned}
a_0 - a_1 + a_2 - a_3 + \ldots &= (1 - E + E^2 - E^3 + \ldots) a_0 \\
&= (1 + E)^{-1} a_0 \\
&= (2 + \Delta)^{-1} a_0 \\
&= \frac{(1 + \Delta/2)^{-1} a_0}{2} \\
&= \frac{(a_0 - \Delta a_0/2 + \Delta^2 a_0/4 - \Delta^3 a_0/8 + \ldots)}{2}.
\end{aligned}
$$

For the above example, $1 - \frac{1}{2} + \frac{1}{3} - \frac{1}{4} + \ldots$, we find that the differences satisfy

$$\Delta^k a_0 = \frac{(-1)^k}{k+1},$$

and hence the first few terms of Euler's rearrangement of this series yield

$$\frac{(1 + \frac{1}{4} + \frac{1}{12} + \frac{1}{32} + \frac{1}{80} + \ldots)}{2} = 0.688\,54.$$

This is indeed a much better estimate of the sum $\ln 2 = 0.693\,15$ than the partial sum $1 - \frac{1}{2} + \frac{1}{3} - \frac{1}{4} + \frac{1}{5} = 0.783\,33$ which is obtained from the same first five terms of the series.

For arbitrary sign patterns, there is often little we can say except in the important case where the series obtained from the absolute values of the terms is convergent.

DEFINITION 3.4.1   The series $\sum a_n$ is said to be **absolutely convergent** if $\sum |a_n|$ is convergent. A series which is convergent but not absolutely convergent is said to be **conditionally convergent**.

Examples 3.4.2

1 Any convergent series of positive terms is absolutely convergent.

2 $\sum (-1)^r/2^r$ is absolutely convergent since $\sum 1/2^r$ is convergent.

3 $\sum (-1)^{n-1}/n$ is conditionally convergent since the harmonic series $\sum 1/n$ diverges.

THEOREM 3.4.2   Any absolutely convergent series is convergent.

Proof Suppose that $\sum u_r$ is absolutely convergent and let

$$v_r = \max(u_r, 0)$$

$$= \begin{cases} u_r & \text{if } u_r \geqslant 0, \\ 0 & \text{if } u_r < 0, \end{cases}$$

$$w_r = -\min(u_r, 0)$$

$$= \begin{cases} 0 & \text{if } u_r \geqslant 0, \\ -u_r & \text{if } u_r < 0. \end{cases}$$

Then $|u_r| \geqslant v_r, w_r \geqslant 0$ for all r and, since $\sum |u_r|$ is convergent, it follows from the comparison test that both $\sum v_r$ and $\sum w_r$ are convergent. Now $u_r = v_r - w_r$ and so $\sum u_r$ is also convergent with sum $\sum v_r - \sum w_r$.

Examples 3.4.3

1 The series $1 - x^2/2! + x^4/4! - \ldots$ is convergent for all values of x. (Therefore, $\cos x$ is defined for all values of x.)
   Denote the terms of the series by u_r. Then $|u_r| = x^{2r}/(2r)! = a_r$, say. Now

$$\frac{a_{r+1}}{a_r} = \frac{x^{2r+2}}{(2r+2)!} \frac{(2r)!}{x^{2r}}$$

$$= \frac{x^2}{(2r+2)(2r+1)}$$

$$\to 0$$

$$< 1$$

so that $\sum a_r = \sum |u_r|$ converges by the ratio test. Thus $\sum u_r$ is absolutely convergent and therefore convergent for every x.

2 $\sum [\sin(rx)]/r^2$ is absolutely convergent and therefore convergent. (Note that this is an example in which the sign pattern could be very irregular depending on the value of x.) Here $|[\sin(rx)]/r^2| \leqslant 1/r^2$ and $\sum 1/r^2$ is convergent. The result follows by the comparison test.

EXERCISES 3.4

1 Which of the series $\sum a_r$ with a_r defined below are absolutely convergent, conditionally convergent or divergent?

(a) $a_r = \dfrac{(-1)^r}{(r+1)(r+2)}$.

(b) $a_r = \dfrac{(-1)^r}{r^{-1/3}}$.

(c) $a_r = \dfrac{(-1)^r(r-1)}{r}$.

(d) $a_r = \dfrac{(-1)^r \ln r}{r}$.

(e) $a_r = \dfrac{\sin(r\pi/2)}{r}$.

(f) $a_r = \dfrac{\cos(rx)}{r^{1/2}}$ for $x = \dfrac{\pi}{4}, \dfrac{\pi}{3}, \dfrac{\pi}{2}$.

2 In Exercises 3.3, **2**, we saw that, if the sequence (a_n) is decreasing and $\sum a_r$ is convergent, then $na_n \to 0$ as $n \to \infty$. Find an example to show that, if the sequence (a_n) is not decreasing, then this conclusion may be invalid; that is, find a convergent series $\sum a_r$ for which $na_n \nrightarrow 0$.

3 Show that, if $\sum a_r$ is absolutely convergent and (b_n) is a bounded sequence, then so is $\sum a_r b_r$. In particular, it follows that $\sum a_r^2$ is absolutely convergent.

3.5 CONVERGENCE OF POWER SERIES

Much of the content of the previous few sections has been leading us to the point at which we can determine the range of values of x for which the sum of a power series $\sum_{r=0}^{\infty} a_r x^r$ is defined, that is, those for which the series converges. Once this **interval of convergence** has been found, we are in a position to examine the convergence in order to decide at what point to truncate the series to achieve the required precision. First we use the ratio test to establish the following theorem.

THEOREM 3.5.1   Suppose that $|a_{n+1}/a_n| \to l > 0$ as $n \to \infty$. Then $\sum_{r=0}^{\infty} a_r x^r$ is absolutely convergent if $|x| < 1/l$ and is divergent if $|x| > 1/l$.

Proof   Let $u_n = |a_n x^n|$. Then

$$\frac{u_{n+1}}{u_n} = \frac{|a_{n+1} x^{n+1}|}{|a_n x^n|}$$

$$= \left| \frac{a_{n+1} x}{a_n} \right|$$

$$\to l|x| \qquad \text{as } n \to \infty.$$

By the ratio test, $\sum u_r$ is convergent if $l|x| < 1$ and divergent if $l|x| > 1$. This completes the proof.

If $|a_{n+1}/a_n| \to 0$, then the series is convergent for all values of x.

DEFINITION 3.5.1   Suppose that $|a_{n+1}/a_n| \to l$; then the number $R = 1/l$ is called the **radius of convergence** of the series $\sum a_r x^r$. If $l = 0$, then we say the series $\sum a_r x^r$ has **infinite radius of convergence** and write $R = \infty$.

The radius of convergence R is thus that number for which $\sum a_r x^r$ converges if $|x| < R$ and diverges if $|x| > R$. To find the complete range of values for which the series converges, the **interval of convergence**, we must also consider the cases $x = \pm R$.

Examples 3.5.1

1 Consider $\sum_{n=1}^{\infty} x^n/n$.

Here, $a_n = 1/n$ so that

$$\left| \frac{a_{n+1}}{a_n} \right| = \frac{n}{n+1} \to 1$$

and so

$$R = 1.$$

Thus $\sum x^n/n$ converges for $|x| < 1$ and diverges for $|x| > 1$. For $x = 1$, the series becomes just $\sum 1/n$ which is divergent while, for $x = -1$, we have $\sum (-1)^n/n$ which is convergent. The interval of convergence is therefore $[-1, 1)$.

2 Now consider $\sum_{r=0}^{\infty} (-1)^n(n+1)x^n/2^n$.

Here,

$$\left| \frac{a_{n+1}}{a_n} \right| = \frac{(n+2)}{2(n+1)}$$

$$\to \frac{1}{2}$$

so that

$$R = 2.$$

With $|x| = 2$, we have either $\sum(n+1)$ or $\sum(-1)^n(n+1)$ both of which are divergent. Thus this series converges for $|x| < 2$ and diverges for $|x| \geqslant 2$.

We are now in a position to re-examine some of the important examples which were used to motivate the discussion of the convergence of series.

Suppose that we wish to compute $e = \exp 1$ to accuracy of four decimal places. Now a simple application of Theorem 3.4.2 shows that the exponential series is absolutely convergent for all x and so we may truncate the series at the appropriate point to obtain the required precision in just the same way as in Example 1.3.2. In this case the first eight terms are seen to be sufficient.

To compute π using the identity

$$\frac{\pi}{4} = \tan^{-1} 1,$$

we make use of the fact that within the radius of convergence of a power series we can integrate the series term by term to obtain the integral of the sum function. Now, for $|t| < 1$, we have

$$\frac{d}{dt}(\tan^{-1} t) = \frac{1}{1+t^2}$$

$$= 1 - t^2 + t^4 - t^6 + \ldots.$$

Integrating the series term by term we get

$$\tan^{-1} x = \int_0^x 1 - t^2 + t^4 - \ldots \, dt$$

$$= x - \frac{x^3}{3} + \frac{x^5}{5} - \frac{x^7}{7} + \ldots. \tag{3.5}$$

The geometric series has a radius of convergence $R = 1$ and this is unchanged by the integration process. (For proofs of these results, see Hawkins (1988).) However, the series in equation (3.5) is also convergent for $x = 1$ by the alternating-sign test and so it follows that

$$\frac{\pi}{4} = 1 - \tfrac{1}{3} + \tfrac{1}{5} - \tfrac{1}{7} + \ldots. \tag{3.6}$$

Now standard single-precision floating-point binary representation allocates 23 bits to the fraction; with the hidden bit, this is equivalent to 24 bits. For a correctly rounded value of $\pi/4$ which lies in $[\tfrac{1}{2}, 1)$ and so has exponent 0, we require an error of at most 2^{-25}.

Here we have an alternating series and so the sum is bracketed by each successive pair of partial sums and the truncation error is bounded by the first neglected term. We thus require N terms where

$$\frac{1}{2N + 1} \leqslant 2^{-25},$$

and so we take $N = 2^{24} = 16\,777\,216$ terms! Of course, we can improve matters somewhat by the use of Euler's method. Using the first five terms of the original series we obtain the approximation $\pi \approx 3.3397$, whereas using these same terms and Euler's rearrangement we get $\pi \approx 3.0984$. The error has therefore been reduced by a factor of about 4. It still looks as though this will be an expensive way to compute π.

This (not very efficient) approach illustrates the need for much more sophisticated computational algorithms. Even using

$$\tan^{-1}\left(\frac{1}{\sqrt{3}}\right) = \frac{\pi}{6},$$

so that

$$\pi = 2\sqrt{3} \sum_{n=0}^{\infty} \frac{(-1)^n}{(2n + 1)3^n}$$

reduces the number of terms needed to $N = 14$—a dramatic saving for little effort! In this particular case the convergence is so rapid that Euler's method yields no improvement.

As a final example of power series approximation methods, we consider a function which is of fundamental importance in statistics—the normal distribution function. Typically, we need to evaluate integrals of the form

$$I(x) = \frac{1}{\sqrt{2\pi}} \int\limits_0^x \exp\left(-\frac{t^2}{2}\right) dt.$$

Note that this integral cannot be obtained analytically. (That is, there is no closed formula in terms of the standard elementary functions for the indefinite integral of this function.) However, we already know that the exponential series is convergent for all values of its argument and so we can integrate the power series expansion of $\exp(-t^2/2)$ term by term to get

$$I(x) = \frac{1}{\sqrt{2\pi}} \int\limits_0^x 1 - \frac{t^2}{2} + \frac{t^4}{4 \times 2!} - \frac{t^6}{8 \times 3!} + \ldots \, dt.$$

$$= \frac{1}{\sqrt{2\pi}} \left(x - \frac{x^3}{3 \times 2} + \frac{x^5}{5 \times 4 \times 2!} - \frac{x^7}{7 \times 8 \times 3!} + \ldots \right)$$

$$= \frac{1}{\sqrt{2\pi}} \sum_{n=0}^{\infty} \frac{(-1)^n x^{2n+1}}{(2n+1)2^n n!},$$

a series which, of course, is also convergent for all values of x—very rapidly so for small values. For example, with $x \leqslant \frac{1}{2}$, we obtain an absolute error less than 10^{-5} using only three terms from which we can conclude that $I(0.5) = 0.1915$ to four decimal places. Of course, for larger values of x, more terms will be needed.

Before leaving the subject of power series approximation, it should be observed that, for many practical situations, we can obtain more accurate approximations much more cheaply by using some alternative representation of the function. This may be simply a rearrangement of the power series as, say, a Chebyshev series or may be in terms of a completely different set of basic functions such as $\cos(nx)$ and $\sin(nx)$ $(n = 0, 1, 2, \ldots)$ which are used for a Fourier series expansion.

EXERCISES 3.5

1 Find the radius and interval of convergence of the power series $\sum a_n x^n$ where

(a) $a_n = \left(-\frac{1}{2}\right)^n$,

(b) $a_n = \frac{1}{n^n}$,

(c) $a_n = n(n+1)$.

2 Show that the series $\sum a_n x^n$ and $\sum n a_n x^{n-1}$ have the same radii of convergence. (This establishes part of the fact that a power series can be integrated or differentiated term by term within its radius of convergence to yield the integral or derivative of the sum function.)

3 Use the geometric series

$$1 + x + x^2 + \ldots = \frac{1}{1-x} \qquad \text{for } |x| < 1$$

and the identity

$$\int_0^x -1/(1-t)\,dt = \ln(1-x)$$

to obtain the power series expansion of $\ln(1-x)$. How many terms of this series are needed to evaluate $\ln(\frac{2}{3})$ to six decimal places?

4 Show that

$$\tanh x = \frac{\exp(2x) - 1}{\exp(2x) + 1}$$

and hence that

$$\tanh^{-1} y = \frac{\ln[(1+y)/(1-y)]}{2}.$$

Write down the power series for $\tanh^{-1} y$ ($|y| < 1$) and use it to obtain $\tanh^{-1}(0.1)$ to five decimal places.

3.6 SERIES SOLUTION OF DIFFERENTIAL EQUATIONS

We finish this chapter with a brief look at the application of power series methods to the important problem of the solution of differential equations. Later on, we shall see other approaches to this.

Often the solution of a linear differential equation with variable coefficients can be found by assuming that the solution can be expressed as a power series. We can then substitute the formal series into the equation to obtain an (infinite) system of equations for the coefficients. Typically this system results in one or more recurrence relations.

Suppose that the second-order differential equation

$$y'' + a(x)y' + b(x)y = 0 \tag{3.7}$$

71

has a solution of the form

$$y = \sum_{r=0}^{\infty} c_r x^r, \tag{3.8}$$

Within its (as yet unknown) radius of convergence, we can differentiate equation (3.8) term by term to get

$$y' = \sum_{r=0}^{\infty} c_r r x^{r-1},$$

$$y'' = \sum_{r=0}^{\infty} c_r r(r-1) x^{r-2}. \tag{3.9}$$

Substituting equations (3.8) and (3.9) into equation (3.7) yields, on comparing coefficients of like powers of x, a recurrence relation for the c_r. Once these are determined, we must then examine the power series for convergence and show that its interval of convergence includes any required domain of definition for the solution y.

The process is best illustrated by examples.

Example 3.6.1

$$xy'' + y' + xy = 0 \qquad y(0) = 1 \quad y'(0) = 0.$$

This is a special case of Bessel's equation which has the general form

$$x^2 y'' + xy' + (x^2 - n^2) y = 0.$$

Now with the formal power series expansion (3.8) for y, we get

$$xy'' + y' + xy = \sum_{r=0}^{\infty} c_r r(r-1) x^{r-1} + \sum_{r=0}^{\infty} c_r r x^{r-1} + \sum_{r=0}^{\infty} c_r x^{r+1}$$

Also, from equation (3.8), $y(0) = c_0$ and so $c_0 = 1$, while $y'(0) = c_1$ so that $c_1 = 0$. Now, comparing coefficients of x^n for $n \geqslant 1$ in the above, we get

$$n(n+1)c_{n+1} + (n+1)c_{n+1} + c_{n-1} = 0$$

from which we deduce that $c_{n+1} = -c_{n-1}/(n+1)^2$. Since $c_1 = 0$, it follows that

$$c_3 = c_5 = \ldots = 0.$$

From $c_0 = 1$, we obtain $c_2 = -1/4$ and then $c_4 = -c_2/16 = 1/(2^2 \times 4^2)$ and, in general,

$$c_{2m} = \frac{(-1)^m}{2^2 \times 4^2 \times \ldots \times (2m)^2}$$

$$= \frac{(-1)^m}{2^{2m}(m!)^2}.$$

Therefore,

$$y = 1 - \frac{x^2}{4} + \frac{x^4}{64} - \frac{x^6}{2304} + \dots.$$

This function is usually denoted by $J_0(x)$ and is called the **Bessel function of the first kind of order 0**.

Since $|c_{2(m+1)}/c_{2m}| = 1/4(m+1)^2 \to 0$ as $m \to \infty$, the above series converges for all values of x^2 and hence for all x. This particular series is very rapidly convergent and just six terms are sufficient to evaluate $y(x)$ with an error less than 2×10^{-6} for all $|x| \leqslant 2$.

The general solution of $xy'' + y' + xy = 0$ is $y(x) = AJ_0(x) + BY_0(x)$ where $Y_0(x)$ is the **Bessel function of the second kind (of order 0)** which arises from the odd-order series here if $c_1 \neq 0$.

For a non-homogeneous differential equation

$$y'' + a(x)y' + b(x)y = f(x),$$

we can adopt one of two basic approaches. Either we must find a **particular integral**, that is, some specific function which satisfies the complete non-homogeneous equation or, if $f(x)$ can itself be represented by a power series, then this can be incorporated into the system of equations for the coefficients. The former approach requires that the full general solution of equation (3.7) is found before any initial conditions can be imposed. The latter method has the advantage that the required solution is found directly although the relations connecting the coefficients may be considerably more complicated.

Example 3.6.2

$$xy'' + y' + xy = x + x^3 \qquad y(0) = 1 \quad y'(0) = 0.$$

On substituting the formal series just as in the previous example, we get

$$\sum_{r=0}^{\infty} c_r r^2 x^{r-1} + \sum_{r=0}^{\infty} c_r x^{r+1} = x + x^3.$$

As before, we get $c_0 = 1$ and $c_1 = 0$ which again implies that $c_{2m+1} = 0$ for all m. Comparing coefficients, we now have

x:
$$4c_2 + c_0 = 1 \Rightarrow c_2 = \frac{1 - c_0}{4},$$

x^3:
$$16c_4 + c_2 = 1 \Rightarrow c_4 = \frac{1 - c_2}{16},$$

and, for $n > 2$,

x^{2n-1}:
$$(2n)^2 c_{2n} + c_{2n-2} = 0 \Rightarrow c_{2n} = -\frac{c_{2n-2}}{(2n)^2}.$$

Thus $c_2 = 0, c_4 = 1/16$ and, for $n > 2, c_{2n} = 4(-1)^n/2^{2n}(n!)^2$ and this solution simplifies to yield

$$y(x) = 4J_0(x) + x^2 - 3.$$

Often this basic method is not sufficiently powerful because a simple power series is not always an appropriate representation. In such situations the **Frobenius method** can be used. The idea is that we assume that the solution can be represented in the form

$$y = \sum_{r=0}^{\infty} c_r x^{m+r},$$

where $c_0 \neq 0$ and the (not necessarily integer) value(s) of m are to be found as part of the solution process.

Example 3.6.3

$$4xy'' + 2y' + y = 0.$$

Suppose that y has the above form. Then

$$y' = \sum (m+r)c_r x^{m+r-1}$$

and

$$y'' = \sum (m+r)(m+r-1)c_r x^{m+r-2}.$$

Substituting these into the differential equation and equating coefficients of x^{m+1}, we get

$$4m(m-1)c_0 + 2mc_0 = 2m(2m-1)c_0 = 0.$$

Since $c_0 \neq 0$, this implies either $m = 0$ or $m = \frac{1}{2}$.

Comparing coefficients of x^{m+r} for $r \geq 1$ gives

$$4(m+r+1)(m+r)c_{r+1} + 2(m+r+1)c_{r+1} + c_r = 0.$$

With $m = 0$ this yields $(2r+2)(2r+1)c_{r+1} + c_r = 0$ so that

$$c_{r+1} = -c_r/(2r+1)(2r+2)$$

from which we obtain $c_r = (-1)^r c_0/(2r)!$. From this solution, we get the series

$$c_0\left(1 - \frac{x}{2!} + \frac{x^2}{4!} - \frac{x^3}{6!} + \dots\right) = c_0 \cos(\sqrt{x}).$$

Similarly, with $m = \frac{1}{2}$, we get for the corresponding coefficients c_r', say, $c_r' = (-1)^r c_0'/(2r+1)!$ and this yields the solution $c_0' \sin(\sqrt{x})$. The general solution is therefore

$$y(x) = A \cos(\sqrt{x}) + B \sin(\sqrt{x}).$$

Note here that both series are convergent for all real x *but* that we can only write the solution in this form for $x \geqslant 0$.

For some non-linear equations, we can obtain a series solution not by comparing coefficients in a formal series (which can easily become a very messy process!) but by assuming a Taylor or MacLaurin series expansion of y and then differentiating the differential equation to find the coefficients. Thus, for example, we could write y as a MacLaurin series

$$y(x) = y(0) + xy'(0) + \frac{x^2 y''(0)}{2!} + \dots$$

and find the values $y'(0)$, $y''(0)$, ... by repeated differentiation.

Example 3.6.4

$$y' = 1 + y^2 \qquad y(0) = 0.$$

Now, from the given equation,

$$y'(0) = 1 + [y(0)]^2$$
$$= 1.$$

Differentiating gives

$$y'' = 2yy' \qquad\qquad y''(0) = 0,$$
$$y^{(3)} = 2(y')^2 + 2yy'' \qquad\qquad y^{(3)}(0) = 2,$$
$$y^{(4)} = 6y'y'' + 2yy^{(3)} \qquad\qquad y^{(4)}(0) = 0,$$
$$y^{(5)} = 2yy^{(4)} + 8y'y^{(3)} + 6(y')^2 \qquad y^{(5)}(0) = 16,$$

Thus

$$y(x) = x + \frac{2x^3}{3!} + \frac{16x^5}{5!} + \dots$$

$$= x + \frac{x^3}{3} + \frac{2x^5}{15} + \dots .$$

In this situation, it is often difficult to spot any pattern in the terms and so to obtain a general form for the terms of the series. This makes the convergence analysis of any such solution that much harder and so it is even more necessary to exercise care over the use of such solutions. We shall consider other, genuinely numerical, methods of solution of differential equations in chapter 6.

EXERCISES 3.6

1 Use the basic method of series solution to obtain the general solution of

$$y'' + x^2 y = 0.$$

Show that $c_2 = c_3 = 0$ and that the general solution can therefore be written in the form $c_0 u(x) + c_1 v(x)$ where the series for u and v each contain only terms in x^{4n}. For what values of x do these series converge?

2 Use the Frobenius method to solve the Bessel equation

$$4x^2 y'' + 4xy' + (4x^2 - 1)y = 0$$

and show that the solution can be written in the form $AJ_{1/2}(x) + BJ_{-1/2}(x)$ where these Bessel functions are defined by

$$J_{1/2}(x) = \left(\frac{2}{\pi x}\right)^{1/2} \sin x,$$

$$J_{-1/2}(x) = \left(\frac{2}{\pi x}\right)^{1/2} \cos x.$$

4 INTERPOLATION AND APPROXIMATE EVALUATION OF FUNCTIONS

4.1 INTRODUCTION

In the last chapter, we studied the power series approach to the approximation of functions and some of its uses. It was mentioned there that this is by no means the only (nor, in many cases, the best) way ot tackling this particular problem. In this chapter, we consider some of the alternatives.

We begin with polynomial interpolation which is based on the idea of finding a polynomial which agrees exactly with some information that we have about the function under consideration. This may be in the form of values of the function at some set of points or may include some values of derivatives of that function. Among the situations in which polynomial interpolation may be useful are those where the only information that we have is in this form; this would be the case if, for example the data are the result of some physical experiment or if, as in the case of a book of logarithmic tables, we are given a table of values of the function.

Traditional polynomial interpolation is not always appropriate, although it gives a useful and instructive approach to approximation. In many circumstances, other methods will prove preferable, and it is helpful to draw a distinction between the approximation of a smooth function whose tabulated values are known very accurately and the situation where the data itself is subject to error. (Most practical problems fall somewhere between these two extremes.) In the former situation, polynomial approximation may be applied with advantage over a wide interval, sometimes using polynomials of moderate or high degree. In the latter case, it is invariably desirable to use low-degree polynomials over restricted ranges. One important technique is that of approximation by cubic splines in which the function is represented by different cubic polynomials in different intervals of the tabulation and this representation is smoothed by enforcing continuity of the first two derivatives throughout the range.

Finally, in this chapter, we consider a rather different approach to the problem of finding approximations to the elementary trigonometric and exponential functions—the CORDIC algorithms which are used in most electronic calculators and some computers for the evaluation of these functions and even for multiplication and division.

Before discussing any of these topics in detail, it is worth making a few introductory remarks about the reasons for the choice of polynomials as the basic tools of most of the elementary approximation schemes. There are two principal reasons. Firstly, any continuous function on a closed interval can be approximated to any required accuracy by a polynomial. Secondly, polynomials are the *only* functions which we can, theoretically at least, evaluate *exactly*.

The first of these is based on a famous theorem of Weierstrass.

THEOREM 4.1.1 Let f be a continuous function on $[a, b]$. Given any $h > 0$, there exists a polynomial $p_{N(h)}$ of degree $N(h)$ such that $|f(x) - p_{N(h)}(x)| < h$ for all $x \in [a, b]$. Thus there exists a sequence of polynomials such that $\| f - p_n \|_\infty \to 0$ as $n \to \infty$.

The second reason also merits further comment. The validity of the statement is left for you to ponder but it is worth spending a few moments on the question of the efficient evaluation of a polynomial. This can be achieved using the following rule.

Horner's rule

Suppose that we wish to evaluate the polynomial expression

$$p(x) = a_n x^n + a_{n-1} x^{n-1} + \ldots + a_1 x + a_0.$$

Then

$$p(x) = \{ \ldots [(a_n x + a_{n-1})x + a_{n-2}]x + \ldots + a_1 \} x + a_0.$$

This can be implemented by the following few simple lines of BASIC program:

```
B(N) = A(N)
FOR I = 1 TO N
  B(N − I) = B(N − I + 1)*X + A(N − I)
NEXT I
```

where the coefficients are held in the array $A(N)$ and the final value $B(0)$ is the required $p(x)$. (Of course, appropriate line numbers would also have to be incorporated into this code.)

Considering this as a piece of hand-calculation we also see that there is a significant saving of effort. In the above routine each of the n steps of the algorithm entails one multiplication and one addition so that the complete calculation is achieved in n multiplications and n additions. However, the direct computation of the polynomial requires much more effort than this; to compute the term $a_i x^i$ requires a total of i multiplications and therefore the whole operation entails $n + (n-1) + \ldots + 2 + 1 = n(n+1)/2$ multiplications in all, together with the n additions required to sum all the terms.

Example 4.1.1

Evaluate

$$p(x) = 6x^5 + 5x^4 + 4x^3 + 3x^2 + 2x + 1$$

for $x = 0.1234$.

By Horner's rule, we get

$$p(x) = (\{[(6x + 5)x + 4]x + 3\}x + 2)x + 1$$
$$= 1.301\,33.$$

The sequence of values which would be generated by the above code are

$$B(5) = A(5)$$
$$= 6,$$
$$B(4) = B(5) \times 0.1234 + A(4)$$
$$= 0.7404 + 5$$
$$= 5.7404,$$
$$B(3) = 5.7404 \times 0.1234 + 4$$
$$= 4.708\,365,$$
$$B(2) = 4.708\,365 \times 0.1234 + 3$$
$$= 3.581\,012,$$
$$B(1) = 3.581\,012 \times 0.1234 + 2$$
$$= 2.441\,897,$$
$$B(0) = 2.441\,897 \times 0.1234 + 1$$
$$= 1.301\,330.$$

We thus see that polynomials offer us both ease of evaluation and arbitrary accuracy of approximation which makes them a natural starting point for interpolation.

4.2 LAGRANGE INTERPOLATION

The basic idea of polynomial interpolation is that we find a polynomial which agrees with the data from the function f of interest. The Lagrange interpolation polynomial has the property that it takes the same value as f on a finite set of distinct points.

Before discussing the details of this it should be noted that you are probably familiar with at least one form of interpolation polynomial. The first $N + 1$ terms of the Taylor expansion of f about a point x_0 form a polynomial of degree N, namely

$$p(x) = f(x_0) + (x - x_0)f'(x_0) + \ldots + \frac{(x - x_0)^N f^{(N)}(x_0)}{N!}$$

which satisfies the **interpolation conditions**

$$p^{(k)}(x_0) = f^{(k)}(x_0) \qquad k = 0, 1, \ldots, N.$$

We also know from Taylor's theorem that the error in using $p(x)$ to approximate $f(x)$ is given by

$$f(x) - p(x) = \frac{f^{(N+1)}(\theta)(x - x_0)^{N+1}}{(N + 1)!}$$

for some θ lying between x and x_0.

Why should we not just settle for this? Firstly, in many data-fitting applications, we are only given function values and the corresponding derivative values are not available; secondly, this approach will usually provide good approximations only near the base point x_0.

This does illustrate, however, the general polynomial interpolation problem; we first find a formula for the polynomial (of minimum degree) with the required properties and then find an expression for the error of the resulting approximation. Of course, this error term will not be an explicitly computable quantity since, if it were, then we could evaluate the function exactly in the first place.

Suppose then that we are given the values of f at the $N + 1$ distinct points $x_0, x_1, \ldots, x_N$. We wish to find the minimum-degree polynomial p such that

$$p(x_k) = f(x_k) \qquad \text{for } k = 0, 1, \ldots, N. \tag{4.1}$$

Suppose that p has degree m. Then we can write

$$p(x) = a_m x^m + a_{m-1} x^{m-1} + \ldots + a_1 x + a_0,$$

where the coefficients $a_0, a_1, \ldots, a_m$ are still to be found. Substituting this expression into equation (4.1) yields the following system of linear equations for $a_0, a_1, \ldots, a_m$:

$$\begin{cases} a_m x_0^m + a_{m-1} x_0^{m-1} + \dots + a_0 = f(x_0), \\ a_m x_1^m + a_{m-1} x_1^{m-1} + \dots + a_0 = f(x_1), \\ \qquad \cdot \quad \cdot \quad \cdot \quad \cdot \quad \cdot \quad \cdot \quad \cdot \quad \cdot \quad \cdot \quad \cdot \quad \cdot \quad \cdot \;, \\ a_m x_N^m + a_{m-1} x_N^{m-1} + \dots + a_0 = f(x_N), \end{cases} \tag{4.2}$$

In general, such a system will have no solution if $m < N$, infinitely many for $m > N$ and, provided that the matrix $\mathbf{A}$ with elements $a_{ij} = x_{i-1}^{j-1}$ is non-singular (which it is), a unique solution if $m = N$. We thus expect our interpolation polynomial to have degree N (or less if it should turn out that $a_N = 0$). Although this approach provides us with a theoretical way of finding the coefficients $a_0, a_1, \dots, a_N$ if this is to be useful, then we require a more convenient route to the solution of equation (4.2).

Now, if we can find polynomials l_j ($j = 0, 1, \dots, N$) of degree at most N such that

$$l_j(x_k) = \delta_{jk} = \begin{cases} 1 & \text{if } j = k, \\ 0 & \text{if } j \neq k, \end{cases} \tag{4.3}$$

then the polynomial p given by

$$p(x) = \sum_{j=0}^{N} f(x_j) l_j(x) \tag{4.4}$$

will have degree at most N and satisfy the interpolation conditions.

The requirement that $l_j(x_k) = 0$ whenever $j \neq k$ means that l_j must have the factors $x - x_k$ for every $k \neq j$. There are N of these factors so that l_j does indeed have degree N. In order that we also obtain $l_j(x_j) = 1$, it follows that l_j is given by

$$l_j(x) = \frac{(x - x_0)(x - x_1)\dots(x - x_{j-1})(x - x_{j+1})\dots(x - x_N)}{(x_j - x_0)(x_j - x_1)\dots(x_j - x_{j-1})(x_j - x_{j+1})\dots(x_j - x_N)}. \tag{4.5}$$

These polynomials are called the **Lagrange basis polynomials** and the polynomial p given by equation (4.4) is the **Lagrange interpolation polynomial**. We have established the existence of this polynomial by finding it although we had already asserted this from our consideration of the simultaneous equations (4.2). These same considerations are also sufficient to demonstrate the uniqueness of the interpolation polynomial of degree at most N satisfying equation (4.1). (All this relies on the stated fact that the matrix $\mathbf{A}$ mentioned earlier is non-singular. The proof of this by showing that the **Vandermonde determinant**, that is,

$$\begin{vmatrix} 1 & x_0 & x_0^2 & \dots & x_0^N \\ 1 & x_1 & x_1^2 & \dots & x_1^N \\ \cdot & \cdot & \cdot & \dots & \cdot \\ 1 & x_N & x_N^2 & \dots & x_N^N \end{vmatrix}$$

does not vanish for $x_0, x_1, \dots, x_N$ distinct is left as an exercise.)

Example 4.2.1

Use the Lagrange interpolation polynomial to estimate the value of $f(1.2)$ from the following data.

x	1	1.5	2
$f(x)$	0.0000	0.4055	0.6931

Here, taking $x_0 = 1$, $x_1 = 1.5$ and $x_2 = 2$, we obtain the quadratic interpolation polynomial

$$p(x) = f(x_0)\frac{(x - x_1)(x - x_2)}{(x_0 - x_1)(x_0 - x_2)} + f(x_1)\frac{(x - x_0)(x - x_2)}{(x_1 - x_0)(x_1 - x_2)}$$

$$+ f(x_2)\frac{(x - x_0)(x - x_1)}{(x_2 - x_0)(x_2 - x_1)}$$

$$= 0.0000\frac{(x - 1.5)(x - 2)}{(1 - 1.5)(1 - 2)}$$

$$+ 0.4055\frac{(x - 1)(x - 2)}{(1.5 - 1)(1.5 - 2)} + 0.6931\frac{(x - 1)(x - 1.5)}{(2 - 1)(2 - 1.5)}.$$

For $x = 1.2$, this yields

$$p(1.2) = \frac{0.4055 \times 0.2 \times 0.8}{0.25} - \frac{0.6931 \times 0.2 \times 0.3}{0.5}$$

$$= 0.1763 \qquad \text{to four decimal places.}$$

As with the Taylor polynomial, we wish to find an expression for the error in this process. This can be fairly readily accomplished by repeated use of Rolle's theorem as follows.

THEOREM 4.2.1   Suppose that the function f is $N + 1$ times continuously differentiable on the interval $[a, b]$ and let $x_0, x_1, \ldots, x_N$ be distinct points in $[a, b]$. Denote by p the Lagrange interpolation polynomial given by equation (4.4). Then, for any $x \in [a, b]$,

$$f(x) - p(x) = \frac{(x - x_0)(x - x_1)\ldots(x - x_N)f^{(N+1)}(\theta)}{(N + 1)!}$$

for some $\theta \in [a, b]$.

Proof Firstly, for simplicity of notation, we denote $(x-x_0)(x-x_1)...(x-x_N)$ by $L(x)$. Now, for $x\in[a,b]$ but not in $\{x_0,x_1,...,x_N\}$, consider the function E defined by

$$E(t)=f(t)-p(t)-cL(t),$$

where the *constant* c is chosen so that $E(x)=0$. It now follows that $E(t)$ vanishes at $N+2$ distinct points $x_0,x_1,...,x_N$ and x. By Rolle's theorem between each successive pair of these there is a point at which E' vanishes. Repeating this argument for $E',E'',...,E^{(N+1)}$, we deduce eventually that there is a point $\theta\in[a,b]$ such that

$$E^{(N+1)}(\theta)=0.$$

However, by differentiating the definition of E, we see that this implies that

$$f^{(N+1)}(\theta)-p^{(N+1)}(\theta)-cL^{(N+1)}(\theta)=0.$$

Now p is a polynomial of degree at most N and so $p^{(N+1)}\equiv 0$ and $L^{(N+1)}\equiv(N+1)!$. Hence $c=f^{(N+1)}(\theta)/(N+1)!$ which with the fact that c is chosen to make $E(x)=0$ completes the proof.

It should be pointed out here that the result remains valid for x outside the interval $[a,b]$ (with slight adjustment to the range of possible values of θ) but that this would cease to be **interpolation**. The process of **extrapolation** in which we attempt to obtain values of the function at points outside the spread of the data is numerically much less satisfactory since the error increases rapidly as x moves away from the interval $[a,b]$.

Generally speaking, we would expect the accuracy to improve as the number of data points, and therefore the degree of the polynomial, increases. The above result does, to some extent, bear this out since the $(N+1)!$ is likely to dominate the numerator of this remainder term *provided that* the high-order derivatives of f remain bounded.

Unfortunately the inclusion of additional data into the Lagrange interpolation polynomial is not a simple matter.

Example 4.2.2

Suppose that for the previous example we had the additional data $f(1.4)=0.3365$. Then the calculation that we did in Example 4.2.1 is of no further benefit and we must start afresh.

We obtain the result

$$p(x)=\frac{0.3365\times 0.048}{0.024}-\frac{0.4055\times 0.032}{0.025}+\frac{0.6931\times 0.012}{0.3}$$

$$=0.1817.$$

The data here were taken from the function $\ln x$ and the true value of $\ln(1.2)$ is 0.1823 to four decimal places; we see that indeed this second result is much more accurate. The formula given by Theorem 4.2.1 implies that the error here is given by $(1.2-1)(1.2-1.4)(1.2-1.5)(1.2-2)f^{(4)}(\theta)/4!$. Now $f^{(4)}(x) = -3!/x^4$; therefore, $|f^{(4)}(\theta)| \leqslant 3!$ and so this error is bounded by $0.0096/4 = 0.0024$.

There are many different ways of representing this interpolation polynomial and we shall see some others in the next section. The principal motivation for this is to find convenient forms which can be programmed and implemented efficiently. Since the polynomial itself is unique, these are all just different ways of writing down the same thing; therefore, we do not need to repeat the error analysis.

As well as the representation, we may also be free to choose the interpolation points themselves. Consideration of the remainder term given in Theorem 4.2.1 shows that it could be advantageous to choose the points so that $L(x)$ is kept as small as possible over the whole interval of interest. It is precisely this which leads to the choice of the Chebyshev interpolation points. For details of this the reader is referred to a more advanced text such as Johnson and Riess (1982).

EXERCISES 4.2

1 Show that the Vandermonde determinant,

$$
\begin{vmatrix}
1 & x_0 & x_0^2 & \cdots & x_0^N \\
1 & x_1 & x_1^2 & \cdots & x_1^N \\
\cdot & \cdot & \cdot & \cdots & \cdot \\
1 & x_N & x_N^2 & \cdots & x_N^N
\end{vmatrix}
$$

does not vanish provided that $x_0, x_1, \ldots, x_N$ are all distinct. (Show that $x_j - x_k$ is a factor of the determinant whenever $j \neq k$.)

2 Consider the following table of values of the cosine function.

x	0.0	0.1	0.2	0.3	0.4	0.5	0.6	0.7	0.8
$\cos x$	1.0000	0.9950	0.9801	0.9553	0.9211	0.8776	0.8253	0.7648	0.6967

Write down the Lagrange interpolation polynomials using the points 0.0,

0.1 and 0.2 and then using 0.3 as well. Estimate the value of $\cos(0.14)$ using each of these polynomials. Obtain a bound for the error in each case.

3 Show that for any $x \in (0.0, 0.8)$ the Lagrange interpolation quadratic using the three nearest points from the above table results in an error of less than 6.5×10^{-5}. Note that the data have slightly greater precision than this.

4 Show that, if $x \in (0.1, 0.7)$, then the Lagrange interpolation polynomial using the four closest points to x from the above table results in an error of less than 5×10^{-6}.

5 Repeat Exercises 4.2, **2** for the function $\ln(1 + x)$ for the same values of x. How many data points will be needed to ensure that using the Lagrange interpolation polynomial will introduce no new errors to four decimal places?

4.3 DIFFERENCE REPRESENTATIONS

In this section, we are concerned with alternative ways of writing down the interpolation polynomials that we discussed in the previous section, which may be more convenient and efficient to program and to use in practice. All the representations which we consider here can be derived from the use of **divided differences** and so we start with their definition.

DEFINITION 4.3.1 The *zeroth-order divided difference* of f at x_k is defined by

$$f[x_k] = f(x_k).$$

The *first-order divided difference* is

$$f[x_k, x_{k+1}] = \frac{f[x_{k+1}] - f[x_k]}{x_{k+1} - x_k}. \tag{4.6}$$

Higher-order divided differences are defined recursively by

$$f[x_k, x_{k+1}, \ldots, x_{k+m}] = \frac{f[x_{k+1}, \ldots, x_{k+m}] - f[x_k, \ldots, x_{k+m-1}]}{x_{k+m} - x_k}. \tag{4.7}$$

Now we see from equation (4.6) that

$$f(x) = f[x_0] + (x - x_0)f[x_0, x] \tag{4.8}$$

and, substituting equation (4.7) into this with $k = 0$ and increasing values of m, we get

85

$$f(x) = f[x_0] + (x - x_0)f[x_0, x]$$
$$= f[x_0] + (x - x_0)f[x_0, x_1] + (x - x_0)(x - x_1)f[x_0, x_1, x]$$
$$= \ldots$$
$$= f[x_0] + (x - x_0)f[x_0, x_1] + (x - x_0)(x - x_1)f[x_0, x_1, x_2] + \ldots \quad (4.9)$$
$$+ (x - x_0)\ldots(x - x_{N-1})f[x_0, x_1, \ldots, x_N]$$
$$+ (x - x_0)\ldots(x - x_N f[x_0, \ldots, x_N, x].$$

If now we write

$$p(x) = f[x_0] + (x - x_0)f[x_0, x_1] + \ldots$$
$$+ (x - x_0)\ldots(x - x_{N-1})f[x_0, x_1, \ldots, x_N] \quad (4.10)$$

which is a polynomial of degree at most N, then for $0 \leqslant k \leqslant N$ we have

$$p(x_k) = f[x_0] + (x_k - x_0)f[x_0, x_1] + \ldots$$
$$+ (x_k - x_0)\ldots(x_k - x_{k-1})f[x_0, x_1, \ldots, x_k]$$

since all the higher-order terms have the factor $x_k - x_k$. Hence, we can prove the following theorem.

THEOREM 4.3.1 The polynomial given by equation (4.10) satisfies the interpolation conditions (4.1), namely

$$p(x_k) = f(x_k) \qquad k = 0, 1, \ldots, N.$$

Proof Now,

$$p(x_k) = f[x_0] + (x_k - x_0)f[x_0, x_1] + \ldots$$
$$+ (x_k - x_0)\ldots(x_k - x_{k-2})f[x_0, x_1, \ldots, x_{k-1}]$$
$$+ (x_k - x_0)\ldots(x_k - x_{k-2})(x_k - x_{k-1})f[x_0, x_1, \ldots, x_k]$$
$$= f[x_0] + (x_k - x_0)f[x_0, x_1] + \ldots$$
$$+ (x_k - x_0)\ldots(x_k - x_{k-2})\{f[x_0, \ldots, x_{k-1}] + \ldots$$
$$+ (x_k - x_{k-1})f[x_0, \ldots, x_{k-1}, x_k]\}$$

but, since

$$(x_k - x_{k-1})f[x_0, \ldots, x_{k-1}, x_k] = f[x_0, \ldots, x_{k-2}, x_k] - f[x_0, \ldots, x_{k-2}, x_{k-1}],$$

this yields

$$p(x_k) = f[x_0] + (x_k - x_0)f[x_0, x_1] + \ldots$$
$$+ (x_k - x_0)\ldots(x_k - x_{k-2})f[x_0, \ldots, x_{k-2}, x_k]$$

and, continuing in this way, we get

$$p(x_k) = f[x_0] + (x_k - x_0)f[x_0, x_1] + \dots$$
$$+ (x_k - x_0)\dots(x_k - x_{k-3})f[x_0,\dots, x_{k-3}, x_k]$$
$$= \dots$$
$$= f[x_0] + (x_k - x_0)f[x_0, x_k]$$
$$= f(x_k),$$

using the equivalent of equation (4.6) for x_0 and x_k.

It follows by the uniqueness of the Lagrange interpolation polynomial that equation (4.10) must be a rearrangement of this polynomial. This particular form is known as **Newton's divided-difference interpolation polynomial**. It is a particularly useful form of the polynomial as it allows the data points to be introduced one at a time without the waste of effort that this entails for the Lagrange form.

Comparison of equations (4.9) and (4.10) shows that the error term for the divided-difference interpolation formula is $(x - x_0)\dots(x - x_N)f[x_0,\dots, x_N, x]$ and, since the polynomial is a rearrangement of the Lagrange polynomial, it follows that the error must also be the same. Thus we see that

$$(x - x_0)\dots(x - x_N)f[x_0,\dots, x_N, x] = \frac{(x - x_0)\dots(x - x_N)f^{(N+1)}(\theta)}{(N+1)!}$$

for some value θ in an interval containing $x_0, x_1,\dots, x_N$ and x.

Example 4.3.1

Use Newton's divided-difference formula to estimate the values $\ln(1.2)$ and $\ln(1.7)$ from the following data.

x	1	1.4	1.5	2
$\ln x$	0.0000	0.3365	0.4055	0.6931

Now, for $x = 1.2$ taking $x_0 = 1$, $x_1 = 1.4$, $x_2 = 1.5$ and $x_3 = 2$, we obtain the following table of divided differences.

k	x_k	$f[x_k]$	$f[x_k, x_{k+1}]$	$f[x_k, x_{k+1}, x_{k+2}]$	$f[x_k, x_{k+1}, x_{k+2}, x_{k+3}]$
0	1.0	0.0000	0.8413	−0.3026	0.1113
1	1.4	0.3365	0.6900	−0.1913	
2	1.5	0.4055	0.5752		
3	2.0	0.6931			

For example, we have obtained 0.69000 from $(0.4055 - 0.3365)/(1.5 - 1.4)$ and -0.3026 from $(0.6900 - 0.8413)/(1.5 - 1.0)$.

This yields the sequence of approximations

$$f\lfloor x_0 \rfloor + (x - x_0)f[x_0, x_1] = 0.168\,26$$

$$= 0.1683 \qquad \text{to four decimal places,}$$

$$0.168\,26 + 0.2 \times (-0.2) \times (-0.3026) = 0.180\,364$$

$$= 0.1804 \qquad \text{to four decimal places,}$$

$$0.180\,36 + 0.2 \times (-0.2) \times (-0.3) \times 0.1113 = 0.181\,699\,6$$

$$= 0.1817 \qquad \text{to four decimal places.}$$

We see immediately the ease of introducing extra data into the calculation and the possibility of proceeding with the process in an iterative way adding in more and more data until successive approximations to the required value agree to some specified tolerance. This provides a highly practical way of avoiding the necessity of finding a bound for the error—usually, a very difficult task!

For $x = 1.7$, it is reasonable to change the order of the data points so that we use those nearest to the point of interest first. Thus, we take $x_0 = 1.5$ and then x_1 could be either 1.4 or 2.0. However, only in the latter case would the first approximation be the result of **interpolation** and so we take $x_1 = 2$, $x_2 = 1.4$ and $x_3 = 1$. The difference table is now as follows.

k	x_k	$f[x_k]$	$f[x_k, x_{k+1}]$	$f[x_k, x_{k+1}, x_{k+2}]$	$f[x_k, x_{k+1}, x_{k+2}, x_{k+3}]$
0	1.5	0.4055	0.5752	−0.1913	0.1114
1	2.0	0.6931	0.5943	−0.2470	
2	1.4	0.3365	0.8413		
3	1.0	0.0000			

This yields the approximations, to four decimal places

$$0.5205, \qquad 0.5320, \qquad 0.5300.$$

The true value of $\ln(1.7) = 0.5306$ to four decimal places.

The following program provides an implementation of divided-difference interpolation. In this particular case, values of the function at four different points are to be estimated and the data are recorded for each one. New points are added into the data being used until either all eight have been used or two successive estimates agree to within the specified tolerance, which in this case is 10^{-3}. At each stage the computation is kept to a minimum by finding the next closest data point and the next set of differences only if they are needed.

PROGRAM 4.3.1

```
10   OPEN "RES.LIS" FOR OUTPUT AS FILE £3
     PRINT £3,"THIS PROGRAM ESTIMATES VALUES OF A FUNCTION USING"
     PRINT £3,"        NEWTON'S DIVIDED DIFFERENCE FORMULA"
     PRINT £3,"TAKING POINTS CLOSEST TO THE REQUIRED ONE FIRST."
     DIM X(7),Y(7),P(8),F(8),D(7,7)
     PRINT £3,
     FOR I = 0 TO 7 \ READ X(I),D(I,0) \ NEXT I
     REM****X(I) AND D(I,0) HOLD THE DATA****
20   E = 1E − 3
     REM****E IS THE TOLERANCE REQUIRED****

50   FOR K = 1 TO 4
       READ X0
       FOR I = 0 TO 7 \ Y(I) = X0 − X(I) \ NEXT I
       PRINT £3,"REQUIRED VALUE IS F(";X0;")"
       P(0) = 1
       F(0) = 0
     REM****P(I) WILL HOLD THE PRODUCT OF THE FACTORS X0 − X(J) FOR J < I****
     REM****F(I) WILL HOLD THE CURRENT ESTIMATE OF F(X0)****

60     FOR I = 0 TO 7
         REM****FIND NEXT CLOSEST DATA POINT TO X0****
61       FOR J = I + 1 TO 7
           IF ABS(Y(J)) < ABS(Y(I)) THEN X = X(I) \ Y = Y(I) \ D = D(I,0)
             X(I) = X(J) \ Y(I) = Y(J) \ D(I,0) = D(J,0)
             X(J) = X \ Y(J) = Y \ D(J,0) = D
70         NEXT J
         P(I + 1) = P(I)*Y(I)
         PRINT £3,X(I),D(I,0),
     REM****COMPUTE NEXT ROW OF DIVIDED DIFFERENCES****
80       FOR J = 1 TO I
           D(I,J) = (D(I,J − 1) − D(I − 1,J − 1)/(X(I) − X(I − J))
81       NEXT J
     REM****ADD IN NEXT TERM TO ESTIMATE OF FUNCTION VALUE****

90       F(I + 1) = F(I) + P(I)*D(I,I)
         PRINT £3,"NEXT ESTIMATE IS";F(I + 1)
         IF I = 0 THEN 100
                 ELSE IF ABS(F(I + 1) − F(I)) < E THEN F = F(I + 1) \ GOTO 120
100    NEXT I
110    PRINT £3,"ALL DATA USED" \ GOTO 130
120    PRINT £3,"CONVERGED. ESTIMATED VALUE F(";X0;") IS";F
130    PRINT £3,
       PRINT £3,
       NEXT K
150  STOP
```

```
200   DATA 1.0,−1.5574,1.1,−1.0296,1.3,−0.4228,1.4,−0.207
201   DATA 1.55,0.1003,1.75,0.5463,1.8,0.6841,2.0,1.5574
202   DATA 1.03,1.25,1.42,1.7

300   END
```

From this program, we obtain the approximate values:

$$f(1.03) \approx -1.3716,$$

$$f(1.25) \approx -0.5458,$$

$$f(1.42) \approx -0.1616,$$

$$f(1.7) \approx 0.4233$$

For $x = 1.42$, the output from the program is

REQUIRED VALUE IS F(1.42)

1.4	−0.2027	NEXT ESTIMATE IS −0.2027
1.3	−0.4228	NEXT ESTIMATE IS −0.15868
1.55	0.1003	NEXT ESTIMATE IS −0.160418
1.1	−1.0296	NEXT ESTIMATE IS −0.161841
1.75	0.5463	NEXT ESTIMATE IS −0.161592

CONVERGED. ESTIMATED VALUE F(1.42) IS −0.161592

Here the two left-hand columns indicate the data being used and the order in which they are included in the calculation while the right-hand column shows the approximations obtained steadily settling down.

There are efficient ways of implementing this to reduce the computational effort further. Amongst these are the algorithms of Aitken and Neville which compute the values of the interpolation polynomials directly without the need for the explicit computation of the divided differences on which they are based. One common situation in which interpolation may be used is the calculation of intermediate values of a function for which we have a table of values—such as in a book of logarithmic tables. The important special feature of this is the fact that the interpolation points are equally spaced. In this special situation the divided differences and the resulting interpolation formulae take on a convenient simple form.

Suppose then that the interpolation points are spaced at regular intervals of length h so that

$$x_n = x_0 + nh \qquad n = \ldots, -2, -1, 0, 1, 2, \ldots . \qquad (4.11)$$

DEFINITION 4.3.2   We define **forward differences** of f at x_r as follows:

first difference: $\Delta f(x_r) = f(x_{r+1}) - f(x_r),$

second difference: $\Delta^2 f(x_r) = \Delta f(x_{r+1}) - \Delta f(x_r)$

$$= f(x_{r+2}) - 2f(x_{r+1}) + f(x_r),$$

90

kth difference: $\qquad \Delta^k f(x_r) = \Delta^{k-1} f(x_{r+1}) - \Delta^{k-1} f(x_r).$

It is not too difficult to show by induction on k that

$$f[x_r, x_{r+1}, \ldots, x_{r+k}] = \frac{\Delta^k f(x_r)}{h^k k!}. \qquad (4.12)$$

Now, writing $x = x_0 + sh$, $f_n = f(x_n)$ and $\Delta^k f_n = \Delta^k f(x_n)$ and substituting into the divided-difference interpolation formula (4.10), we get

$$f(x_0 + sh) \approx f[x_0] + (x - x_0)f[x_0, x_1] + (x - x_0)(x - x_1)f[x_0, x_1, x_2] + \cdots$$

$$= f_0 + \frac{sh\Delta f_0}{h} + \frac{s(s-1)h^2 \Delta^2 f_0}{h^2 2!} + \cdots$$

$$= f_0 + s\Delta f_0 + \frac{s(s-1)\Delta^2 f_0}{2!} + \cdots \qquad (4.13)$$

Example 4.3.2

Estimate the value of $\ln(1.13)$ from the following table.

x	1.0	1.1	1.2	1.3	1.4	1.5	1.6	1.7
$\ln x$	0.0000	0.0953	0.1823	0.2624	0.3365	0.4055	0.4700	0.5306

In much the same way as for the divided-difference formula, we begin by forming the difference table as follows.

x	f	Δf	$\Delta^2 f$	$\Delta^3 f$	$\Delta^4 f$
1.0	0.0000				
		0.0953			
1.1	0.0953		−0.0083		
		0.0870		0.0014	
1.2	0.1823		−0.0069		−0.0005
		0.0801		0.0009	
1.3	0.2624		−0.0060		0.0000
		0.0741		0.0009	
1.4	0.3365		−0.0051		−0.0003
		0.0690		0.0006	
1.5	0.4055		−0.0045		0.0000
		0.0645		0.0006	
1.6	0.4700		−0.0039		
		0.0606			
1.7	0.5306				

In this, each entry is obtained simply as the difference of the two entries immediately to its left.

Now **Newton's forward-difference interpolation formula** (4.13) requires that we decide on the base point x_0 and introduce the points $x_1, x_2, \ldots$ in turn. Thus we are not in a position, with this formula, to use the points in the order of their proximity to the point of interest. The choice of x_0 is therefore important.

First, we consider the choice $x_0 = 1.1$, that is, the closest data point to 1.13. Then, since $h = 0.1$, we have $1.13 = x_0 + 0.3h$ and so $s = 0.3$. The sequence of estimates of $\ln(1.13)$ obtained from equation (4.13) are therefore

$$\ln(1.13) \approx f_0 = 0.0953,$$

$$\ln(1.13) \approx f_0 + s\,\Delta f_0$$
$$= 0.0953 + 0.3 \times 0.087$$
$$= 0.1214$$

$$\ln(1.13) \approx f_0 + s\,\Delta f_0 + \frac{s(s-1)\Delta^2 f_0}{2}$$
$$= 0.1214 + \frac{0.3 \times (-0.7) \times (-0.0069)}{2}$$
$$= 0.122\,125,$$

$$\ln(1.13) \approx f_0 + s\,\Delta f_0 + \frac{s(s-1)\Delta^2 f_0}{2} + \frac{s(s-1)(s-2)\Delta^3 f_0}{6}$$
$$= 0.122\,125 + \frac{0.3 \times (-0.7) \times (-1.7) \times 0.0009}{6}$$
$$= 0.122\,178,$$

and, since to the accuracy of the data the next difference is 0, no improvement will be obtained by including further terms. (Subsequent differences could be calculated and incorporated into the approximation but, in this case, any higher-order differences are dominated by the rounding errors in the initial data and are thus unlikely to offer any improvement. For example, the term using the fifth difference would be negative while the true value of $\ln(1.13)$ is greater than this estimate.)

If instead we take $x_0 = 1.0$ in which case $s = 1.3$, then the first two approximations may be less accurate since we would then be using extrapolation. We get the following sequence of estimates:

$$\ln(1.13) \approx f_0 = 0.0000,$$
$$\ln(1.13) \approx f_0 + s\,\Delta f_0$$
$$= 0.123\,89,$$

$$\ln(1.13) \approx f_0 + s\,\Delta f_0 + \frac{s(s-1)\Delta^2 f_0}{2}$$

$$= 0.122\,272,$$

$$\ln(1.13) \approx f_0 + s\,\Delta f_0 + \frac{s(s-1)\Delta^2 f_0}{2} + \frac{s(s-1)(s-2)\Delta^3 f_0}{6}$$

$$= 0.122\,208,$$

and we see that the correct result, to four decimal places, has been obtained.

This improvement can be explained by the fact that, by the time that we used the fourth difference (and therefore four interpolation points), the data being used were taken from the points 1.0, 1.1, 1.2 and 1.3 which are the four closest points in the table to the point of interest 1.13. However, of course at the start of the computation we do now know how many (and therefore which) interpolation points will be needed and so it is desirable to find a way of combining the advantages of the equal spacing of the data points with those of using the closest points first.

We thus want to find a **finite-difference** formula such that $x \in [x_0, x_1]$ and the interpolation points are used in the order $x_0, x_1, x_{-1}, x_2, x_{-2}, \ldots$. This can again be achieved starting from the divided-difference formula (4.10):

$$f(x_0 + sh) \approx f[x_0] + (x-x_0)f[x_0,x_1] + (x-x_0)(x-x_1)f[x_{-1},x_0,x_1] + \cdots$$

$$= f_0 + s\,\Delta f_0 + \frac{s(s-1)\Delta^2 f_{-1}}{2!} + \frac{s(s-1)(s+1)\Delta^3 f_{-1}}{3!} + \cdots \quad (4.14)$$

The general term of this series for an *even*-order difference is

$$\frac{(s+m-1)(s+m-2)\ldots(s+1)s(s-1)\ldots(s-m+1)(s-m)\Delta^{2m}f_{-m}}{(2m)!}$$

while that for an *odd*-order difference is

$$\frac{(s+m)(s+m-1)\ldots(s+1)s(s-1)\ldots(s-m+1)(s-m)\Delta^{2m+1}f_{-m}}{(2m+1)!}.$$

The effect of this is that we use entries from the difference table which lie close to the horizontal line corresponding to the required value of x.

Example 4.3.3

Use the data of Example 4.3.2 to estimate $\ln(1.34)$.

x	f	Δf	$\Delta^2 f$	$\Delta^3 f$	$\Delta^4 f$
1.0	0.0000				
		0.0953			
1.1	0.0953		-0.0083		
		0.0870		0.0014	
1.2	0.1823		-0.0069		-0.0005
		0.0801		0.0009	
1.3	**0.2624**		**-0.0060**		0.0000
		0.0741		**0.0009**	
1.4	0.3365		-0.0051		-0.0003
		0.0690		0.0006	
1.5	0.4055		-0.0045		0.0000
		0.0645		0.0006	
1.6	0.4700		-0.0039		
		0.0606			
1.7	0.5306				

We take $x_0 = 1.3$, $x_1 = 1.4$ and $s = 0.4$ and then use the data in the order $1.3, 1.4, 1.2, 1.5, \ldots$ to obtain the approximations

$$\ln(1.34) \approx f_0$$

$$= 0.2624,$$

$$\ln(1.34) \approx f_0 + s\,\Delta f_0$$

$$= 0.2624 + 0.4 \times 0.0741$$

$$= 29204,$$

$$\ln(1.34) \approx f_0 + s\,\Delta f_0 + \frac{s(s-1)\,\Delta^2 f_{-1}}{2}$$

$$= 0.29204 + \frac{0.4 \times (-0.6) \times (-0.006)}{2}$$

$$= 0.29276,$$

$$\ln(1.34) \approx 0.29276 + \frac{1.4 \times 0.4 \times (-0.6) \times 0.0009}{6}$$

$$= 0.292710,$$

which again gives the correct result to an accuracy of four decimal places in the data. The differences used are those in *bold* type.

Frequently this interpolation formula, **Gauss's central-difference formula**, is written down using central differences such as $\delta f_{1/2} = f_1 - f_0$ rather than the forward differences that we have used here. However, for our present purposes the forward-difference version is sufficient.

In introducing this approach to finite-difference interpolation, we assumed that x_0 was chosen so that $x \in [x_0, x_1]$. If x itself lies closer to x_1 than to x_0, however, then the order of use of the data points is not quite what was sought since x_2 would be closer to x than x_{-1}. In such a situation, we could choose x_0 so that $x \in [x_{-1}, x_0]$ and use the interpolation points in the order $x_0, x_{-1}, x_{-2}, \ldots$. This leads to a similar expression for the interpolation polynomial to that above.

There are problems associated with polynomial interpolation, however. For the most part, these arise from the fact that, if the number of points used is large, then typically a natural phenomenon which does not have high-degree polynomial behaviour is being represented by just such a function. The combination of this and the fact that such methods are often computationally expensive motivates the search for alternative techniques.

EXERCISES 4.3

1 Use the divided-difference interpolation formula to estimate $f(0.24)$ from the data:

$$f(0) = 6.021,$$

$$f(0.2) = 6.232,$$

$$f(0.3) = 6.335,$$

$$f(0.4) = 6.435,$$

$$f(0.6) = 6.628.$$

2 Modify Program 4.3.1 to find the values of $\cos(0.14)$, $\cos(0.35)$ and $\cos(0.68)$ from the following data.

x	0.0	0.1	0.2	0.3	0.4	0.5	0.6	0.7	0.8
$\cos x$	1.0000	0.9950	0.9801	0.9553	0.9211	0.8776	0.8253	0.7648	0.6967

Note that there are more data points here than in the original program and so the limits on several of the loops will need to be changed.

3 Use induction on k to prove equation (4.12), namely

$$f[x_r, x_{r+1}, \ldots, x_{r+k}] = \frac{\Delta^k f(x_r)}{h^k k!}.$$

4 Use Newton's forward-difference formula to estimate $\cos(0.14)$ and the central-difference formula to find $\cos(0.35)$ and $\cos(0.68)$ from the data in Exercises 4.3, **2**.

5 Write a program to implement the central-difference interpolation formula. Test it by finding the values of $f(0.24)$ and $f(0.37)$ from the following data.

$$f(0) = 6.021,$$
$$f(0.1) = 6.128,$$
$$f(0.2) = 6.232,$$
$$f(0.3) = 6.335,$$
$$f(0.4) = 6.435,$$
$$f(0.5) = 6.532,$$
$$f(0.6) = 6.628.$$

4.4 SPLINES

It was pointed out in the introduction to this chapter that interpolation with a single polynomial is not always an appropriate technique for the approximate evaluation of a function, especially if the number of data points is large or if the data are themselves subject to experimental error. Finite-difference or divided-difference interpolation formulae alleviate some of these problems by using only those interpolation points close to the point of interest. Effectively therefore these methods approximate the function by different low-order polynomials in different intervals.

It will often be more efficient to have a single simple function which can be used to obtain approximate function values throughout the range. The approach described in this section is to use **spline** functions.

DEFINITION 4.4.1   Let $a = x_0 < x_1 < \ldots < x_n = b$. A function $s : [a, b] \to R$ is a **spline** or **spline function** of degree m with **knots** (or interpolation points) $x_0, x_1, \ldots, x_n$ if

(a) s is a *piecewise polynomial* such that, on each subinterval $[x_k, x_{k+1}]$, s has degree at most m and
(b) s is $m - 1$ times differentiable everywhere.

Such a function can therefore be defined by a different polynomial formula on each of the intervals $[x_k, x_{k+1}]$ and hence can be differentiated as often as we like at all points in (x_k, x_{k+1}) for every k. The important extra property is thus the continuity of the various derivatives *at the knots* themselves. We shall consider the detailed implications of these conditions shortly. The idea of spline functions is one which is quite familiar. For example, in many graphical representations of economic indicators such as the rate of inflation or the *Financial Times* index, we see the familiar picture of straight lines joining the dots which represent the actual known data points. This is simply a spline of degree 1, that is, a function which in each of the subintervals is a straight line—a polynomial of degree 1—and is continuous across the joins.

It turns out that interpolation using low-degree spline functions can provide very good and economical methods for the approximate evaluation of a function. We begin by examining splines of degree 1 and then go on to the important special case of cubic splines.

Suppose then that we are given the values of the function f at the points

$$a = x_0 < x_1 < \ldots < x_n = b$$

and that we seek the **linear spline** s which satisfies

$$s(x_k) = f(x_k) \qquad k = 0, 1, \ldots, n. \tag{4.15}$$

In the interval $[x_k, x_{k+1}]$, s must be a polynomial of degree 1 and its graph must pass through the points $(x_k, f(x_k))$ and $(x_{k+1}, f(x_{k+1}))$. This line is given by

$$y = f_k + \frac{f_{k+1} - f_k}{x_{k+1} - x_k}(x - x_k) \qquad x_k \leqslant x \leqslant x_{k+1}, \tag{4.16}$$

where, as before, we use f_k to denote $f(x_k)$. We can use equation (4.16) for $k = 0, 1, \ldots, n-1$ to define the required spline function s. In the case of linear spline interpolation, we thus see that it is easy to write down expressions for the coefficients of the various components of the spline function. For general splines, this is not so straightforward. It is common to use the notation s_k for the component of s which applies to the interval $[x_k, x_{k+1}]$ and to write, for the linear case,

$$s_k(x) = a_k + b_k(x - x_k).$$

From equation (4.16), we obtain

$$a_k = f_k$$

and

$$b_k = \frac{f_{k+1} - f_k}{x_{k+1} - x_k}$$

$$= f[x_k, x_{k+1}].$$

Example 4.4.1

Find the linear spline which takes the following values.

x	0.0	0.2	0.3	0.5
$f(x)$	0.00	0.18	0.26	0.41

Here $x_0 = 0.0$, $x_1 = 0.2$, $x_2 = 0.3$, $x_3 = 0.5$ and so

$$a_0 = 0.00,$$
$$a_1 = 0.18,$$
$$a_2 = 0.26$$

and

$$b_0 = \frac{0.18 - 0.00}{0.2 - 0.0}$$
$$= 0.9,$$
$$b_1 = \frac{0.26 - 0.18}{0.3 - 0.2}$$
$$= 0.8$$
$$b_2 = \frac{0.41 - 0.26}{0.5 - 0.3}$$
$$= 0.75.$$

Thus, we have

$$s(x) = \begin{cases} 0.00 + 0.9(x - 0.0) = 0.9x & 0.0 \leqslant x \leqslant 0.2, \\ 0.18 + 0.8(x - 0.2) = 0.8x + 0.02 & 0.2 \leqslant x \leqslant 0.3, \\ 0.26 + 0.75(x - 0.3) = 0.75x + 0.035 & 0.3 \leqslant x \leqslant 0.5. \end{cases}$$

Note that there is no ambiguity in this definition at, say, $x = 0.2$ since the continuity of s ensures that $s_0(0.2) = s_1(0.2) = 0.18$. Note too that the linear spline is not even defined outside the range of the data as extrapolation using such a function would be especially suspect. In this case the data were again taken from the function $\ln(1 + x)$ and, by contrast with the last remark, the graphs of this function and of the above linear spline would be virtually indistinguishable over the interval $[0.0, 0.5]$.

Probably the most commonly used spline functions are **cubic splines,** whose components are given by

$$s_k(x) = a_k + b_k(x - x_k) + c_k(x - x_k)^2 + d_k(x - x_k)^3. \qquad (4.17)$$

Now s must satisfy the interpolation conditions

$$s(x_k) = f(x_k) \qquad k = 0, 1, \ldots, n \qquad (4.18)$$

and the continuity conditions

$$s_k(x_{k+1}) = s_{k+1}(x_{k+1}) \qquad k = 0, 1, \ldots, n - 2, \qquad (4.19a)$$

$$s_k'(x_{k+1}) = s_{k+1}'(x_{k+1}) \qquad k = 0, 1, \ldots, n - 2, \qquad (4.19b)$$

$$s_k''(x_{k+1}) = s_{k+1}''(x_{k+1}) \qquad k = 0, 1, \ldots, n - 2. \qquad (4.19c)$$

To define our cubic spline s fully, we require the values of the coefficients a_k, b_k, c_k and d_k for $k = 0, 1, \ldots, n - 1$. Thus, we must determine $4n$ coefficients; now equations (4.18) and (4.19) provide us with $(n + 1) + 3(n - 1)$ equations which is therefore two too few. It follows that in the definition of cubic interpolating splines there are two *degrees of freedom.* There are several ways of using this freedom in the definition; we shall consider just one of these, the **natural cubic spline.**

Firstly, the interpolation conditions $s_k(x_k) = f_k$ imply (just as for the linear spline) that

$$a_k = f_k \qquad k = 0, 1, \ldots, n - 1. \qquad (4.20)$$

Substituting this and equation (4.17) into the continuity conditions (4.19a), we get

$$a_k + b_k(x_{k+1} - x_k) + c_k(x_{k+1} - x_k)^2 + \ldots$$
$$+ d_k(x_{k+1} - x_k)^3 = f_{k+1} \qquad k = 0, 1, \ldots, n - 2.$$

We can extend this to $k = n - 1$ and so include the final interpolation condition. Denoting the step lengths by h_k so that

$$h_k = x_{k+1} - x_k \qquad k = 0, 1, \ldots, n - 1,$$

we can rearrange these equations as

$$b_k h_k + c_k h_k^2 + d_k h_k^3 = f_{k+1} - f_k \qquad k = 0, 1, \ldots, n - 1$$

or, dividing throughout by h_k, we get

$$b_k + c_k h_k + d_k h_k^2 = f[x_k, x_{k+1}] = \delta_k, \text{ say}, \qquad k = 0, 1, \ldots, n - 1.$$
$$(4.21)$$

Substituting next into equation (4.19b), we get

$$b_k + 2c_k h_k + 3d_k h_k^2 = b_{k+1} \qquad k = 0, 1, \ldots, n - 2, \qquad (4.22)$$

while from equation (4.19c) we get

$$2c_k + 6d_k h_k = 2c_{k+1} \qquad k = 0, 1, \ldots, n-2.$$

This last equation gives us

$$d_k = \frac{c_{k+1} - c_k}{3h_k} \qquad k = 0, 1, \ldots, n-2, \qquad (4.23)$$

and subtracting equation (4.22) from equation (4.21) results in

$$b_{k+1} = c_k h_k + 2d_k h_k^2 + \delta_k$$

$$= c_k h_k + \frac{2h_k(c_{k+1} - c_k)}{3} + \delta_k$$

$$= \frac{(2c_{k+1} + c_k)h_k}{3} + \delta_k \qquad k = 0, 1, \ldots, n-2,$$

so that

$$b_k = \frac{(2c_k + c_{k-1})h_{k-1}}{3} + \delta_{k-1} \qquad k = 1, 2, \ldots, n-1. \qquad (4.24)$$

Substituting this and equation (4.23) into equation (4.21) for $k = 1, 2, \ldots, n-2$ (for which all are valid) we have

$$\delta_k = \frac{(2c_k + c_{k-1})h_{k-1}}{3} + \delta_{k-1} + c_k h_k + \frac{(c_{k+1} - c_k)h_k}{3}$$

which can be rearranged as

$$h_{k-1}c_{k-1} + 2(h_{k-1} + h_k)c_k + h_k c_{k+1} = 3(\delta_k - \delta_{k-1}) \qquad k = 1, 2, \ldots, n-2.$$
$$(4.25)$$

Writing this system of equations in full, we get

$$
\begin{aligned}
h_0 c_0 + 2(h_0 + h_1)c_1 + h_1 c_2 &= 3(\delta_1 - \delta_0), \\
h_1 c_1 + 2(h_1 + h_2)c_2 + h_2 c_3 &= 3(\delta_2 - \delta_1), \\
h_2 c_2 + 2(h_2 + h_3)c_3 + h_3 c_4 &= 3(\delta_3 - \delta_2),
\end{aligned}
$$

. . . .

$$h_{n-3}c_{n-3} + 2(h_{n-3} + h_{n-2})c_{n-2} + h_{n-2}c_{n-1} = 3(\delta_{n-2} - \delta_{n-3}),$$

which we see is a **tridiagonal** system of $n-2$ linear equations in the n unknowns $c_0, c_1, \ldots, c_{n-1}$. Once *all* these coefficients are determined, then the values of $b_1, b_2, \ldots, b_{n-1}$ and of $d_0, d_1, \ldots, d_{n-2}$ can be obtained from equations (4.23) and (4.24). Then b_0 is given, using equation (4.22), by $b_1 - 2c_0 h_0 - 3d_0 h_0^2$. It is necessary therefore to augment the system (4.25) with two further equations so that the coefficients $c_0, c_1, \ldots, c_{n-1}$ are completely determined.

DEFINITION 4.4.2 The **natural cubic spline** is defined by imposing the extra conditions

$$s''(a) = s''(b) = 0.$$

Now

$$s''(a) = s_1''(x_0)$$
$$= 2c_0$$

and so

$$c_0 = 0,$$

while

$$s''(b) = s_{n-1}''(x_n)$$
$$= 2c_{n-1} + 6d_{n-1}h_{n-1}$$
$$= 0.$$

The second of these conditions is conveniently handled by introducing the spurious coefficient $c_n = 0$ so that

$$d_{n-1} = \frac{-c_{n-1}}{3h_{n-1}}$$
$$= \frac{c_n - c_{n-1}}{3h_{n-1}}$$

or, in other words, equation (4.23) is valid for $k = n - 1$ as well. Hence we obtain, on substituting into equation (4.21) with $k = n - 1$,

$$h_{n-2}c_{n-2} + 2(h_{n-2} + h_{n-1})c_{n-1} = 3(\delta_{n-1} - \delta_{n-2}).$$

The full system thus becomes

$$
\begin{aligned}
2(h_0 + h_1)c_1 + h_1 c_2 &= 3(\delta_1 - \delta_0),\\
h_1 c_1 + 2(h_1 + h_2)c_2 + h_2 c_3 &= 3(\delta_2 - \delta_1),\\
h_2 c_2 + 2(h_2 + h_3)c_3 + h_3 c_4 &= 3(\delta_3 - \delta_2), \quad (4.26)
\end{aligned}
$$

$$\cdots \cdots \cdots \cdots \cdots \cdots \cdots \cdots \cdots \cdots \cdots \cdots$$

$$
\begin{aligned}
h_{n-3}c_{n-3} + 2(h_{n-3} + h_{n-2})c_{n-2} + h_{n-2}c_{n-1} &= 3(\delta_{n-2} - \delta_{n-3}),\\
h_{n-2}c_{n-2} + 2(h_{n-2} + h_{n-1})c_{n-1} &= 3(\delta_{n-1} - \delta_{n-2}),
\end{aligned}
$$

which now has $n - 2$ equations in the remaining $n - 2$ unknowns.

Example 4.4.2

Find the natural cubic spline which fits the following data.

x	25	36	49	64	81
$f(x)$	5	6	7	8	9

Here we have five data points x_0, x_1, x_2, x_3 and x_4 so that $n = 4$ and we expect to obtain a (tridiagonal) 3×3 system of equations.

Firstly $a_k = f_k$ for $k = 0, 1, 2, 3$ so that $a_0 = 5$, $a_1 = 6$, $a_2 = 7$ and $a_3 = 8$.

The step lengths are $h_0 = 11$, $h_1 = 13$, $h_2 = 15$ and $h_3 = 17$ and so the divided differences are $\delta_0 = 1/11 = 0.0909$, $\delta_1 = 0.0769$, $\delta_2 = 0.0667$ and $\delta_3 = 0.0588$ to four decimal places. We thus obtain the system

$$2(11 + 13)c_1 + 13c_2 \qquad = 3(0.0769 - 0.0909) = -0.0420,$$

$$13c_1 + 2(13 + 15)c_2 + 15c_3 = 3(0.0667 - 0.0769) = -0.0306,$$

$$15c_2 + 2(15 + 17)c_3 \qquad = 3(0.0588 - 0.0667) = -0.0237,$$

or in matrix terms

$$\begin{pmatrix} 48 & 13 & 0 \\ 13 & 56 & 15 \\ 0 & 15 & 64 \end{pmatrix} \begin{pmatrix} c_1 \\ c_2 \\ c_3 \end{pmatrix} = \begin{pmatrix} -0.0420 \\ -0.0306 \\ -0.0237 \end{pmatrix}$$

which has the solution

$$c_1 = -0.799 \times 10^{-3},$$
$$c_2 = -0.279 \times 10^{-3},$$
$$c_3 = -0.305 \times 10^{-3}$$

from which we obtain

$$d_0 = -0.242 \times 10^{-4},$$
$$d_1 = 0.133 \times 10^{-4},$$
$$d_2 = -0.578 \times 10^{-6},$$
$$d_3 = 0.598 \times 10^{-5},$$

$$b_1 = 0.850 \times 10^{-1},$$

$$b_2 = 0.710 \times 10^{-1},$$

$$b_3 = 0.622 \times 10^{-1}$$

and then

$$b_0 = 0.938 \times 10^{-1}.$$

Thus the interpolatory natural cubic spline for the above data is given by

$$s(x) = \begin{cases} 5 + 0.0938(x-25) - 0.242 \times 10^{-4}(x-25)^3 & 25 \leqslant x \leqslant 36, \\ 6 + 0.0850(x-36) - 0.799 \times 10^{-3}(x-36)^2 + 0.133 \times 10^{-4}(x-36)^3 & 36 \leqslant x \leqslant 49, \\ 7 + 0.0710(x-49) - 0.279 \times 10^{-3}(x-49)^2 - 0.578 \times 10^{-6}(x-49)^3 & 49 \leqslant x \leqslant 64, \\ 8 + 0.0622(x-64) - 0.305 \times 10^{-3}(x-64)^2 + 0.598 \times 10^{-6}(x-64)^3 & 64 \leqslant x \leqslant 81. \end{cases}$$

This leads, for example, to the approximations

$$\sqrt{30} \approx 5 + 0.0938 \times 5 - 0.242 \times 10^{-4} \times 125 = 5.466 \text{ to 3 decimal places,} \qquad \text{error} \approx 11 \times 10^{-3};$$

$$\sqrt{40} \approx 6 + 0.0850 \times 4 - 0.799 \times 10^{-3} \times 4^2 + 0.133 \times 10^{-4} \times 4^3 = 6.328, \qquad \text{error} \approx 4 \times 10^{-3}.$$

In the above example, we see that the errors are larger than would be expected from using a cubic interpolation polynomial in each subinterval. One of the primary reasons for this is that the matching conditions mean that distant data have some effect on the result. Spline interpolation is thus better suited to the situation where there are many data points and each polynomial component is used over a relatively small range, or one over which the function does not vary too rapidly. These considerations make it plain that the choice of the knots (where we have the freedom to choose them) can be of great importance in obtaining efficient approximations from spline interpolation. We do not dwell on this here but simply observe that the general rule is that more points are needed in regions of rapid change—particularly in the first derivative.

As with ordinary polynomial interpolation, it is worth considering the special case where the data points are equally spaced. Suppose then that

$$h = \frac{b-a}{n}$$

and

$$x_0 = a,$$

$$x_k = x_0 + kh \qquad k = 1, 2, \ldots, n.$$

The system of equations (4.26) then becomes, on dividing throughout by h,

$$4c_1 + c_2 \qquad\qquad = \frac{3(\delta_1 - \delta_0)}{h},$$

$$c_1 + 4c_2 + c_3 \qquad = \frac{3(\delta_2 - \delta_1)}{h},$$

$$c_2 + 4c_3 + c_4 \qquad = \frac{3(\delta_3 - \delta_2)}{h},$$

$$\cdots\cdots\cdots\cdots\cdots\cdots\cdots\cdots\cdots\cdots \qquad\qquad (4.27)$$

$$c_{n-3} + 4c_{n-2} + c_{n-1} = \frac{3(\delta_{n-2} - \delta_{n-3})}{h},$$

$$c_{n-2} + 4c_{n-1} \qquad = \frac{3(\delta_{n-1} - \delta_{n-2})}{h}.$$

We shall see later that special algorithms for the solution of such systems of equations can be designed to take account of the *sparseness* of the matrix of coefficients.

Before leaving the topic of splines, it is of interest to explain the origin of this somewhat intriguing term. Most mathematical terminology is derived from everyday language, taking words which have some similar meaning in common usage and this is—or perhaps *was*—no exception. A spline is a draughtsman's tool originally consisting of a thin strip of wood (more commonly nowadays plastic) which is laid on its edge and constrained to pass through the required points. The resulting shape then provides the draughtsman with a smooth curve connecting these points; this natural curve is a natural cubic spline. Physically the curve so formed can be interpreted as that which minimises the stored energy; this results in the spline assuming the shape with minimum overall curvature.

EXERCISES 4.4

1 Which of the following are splines of degree 1, 2 or 3?

(a) $s(x) = \begin{cases} x & 0 \leqslant x \leqslant 1, \\ 2x - 1 & 1 \leqslant x \leqslant 2, \\ x + 2 & 2 \leqslant x \leqslant 4. \end{cases}$

(b) $s(x) = \begin{cases} 2 - x & 0 \leqslant x \leqslant 1, \\ 2x - 1 & 1 \leqslant x \leqslant 2, \\ x + 1 & 2 \leqslant x \leqslant 4. \end{cases}$

(c) $s(x) = \begin{cases} x^2 & -1 \leqslant x \leqslant 1, \\ 2x^2 - 2x + 1 & 1 \leqslant x \leqslant 2, \\ 3x^2 - 6x + 5 & 2 \leqslant x \leqslant 3. \end{cases}$

(d) $s(x) = \begin{cases} x^3 & 0 \leqslant x \leqslant 1, \\ 2x^2 - 2x + 1 & 1 \leqslant x \leqslant 2, \\ 3x^2 - 6x + 5 & 2 \leqslant x \leqslant 3. \end{cases}$

(e) $s(x) = \begin{cases} x & -1 \leqslant x \leqslant 0, \\ x + x^3 & 0 \leqslant x \leqslant 1, \\ 1 - 2x + 3x^2 & 1 \leqslant x \leqslant 4. \end{cases}$

2 Find the natural cubic interpolating spline for the following data.

x	1	2	3	4	5
$\ln x$	0.0000	0.6931	1.0986	1.3863	1.6094

As usual, the coefficients a_0, a_1, a_2, a_3 are given by the function values themselves:

$$a_0 = 0.0000,$$
$$a_1 = 0.6931,$$
$$a_2 = 1.0986,$$
$$a_3 = 1.3863.$$

From equation (4.27), c_1, c_2 and c_3 are the solutions of the equations

$$\begin{pmatrix} 4 & 1 & 0 \\ 1 & 4 & 1 \\ 0 & 1 & 4 \end{pmatrix} \begin{pmatrix} c_1 \\ c_2 \\ c_3 \end{pmatrix} = \begin{pmatrix} -0.2876 \\ -0.1178 \\ -0.0646 \end{pmatrix}$$

4.5 CORDIC ALGORITHMS

In this section, we concentrate on a topic which is in many ways the modern equivalent of finite-difference interpolation in logarithmic or trigonometric tables. Such techniques are still needed for some special functions and as a basis for numerical integration and solution of differential equations but the elementary functions such as ln, exp, sin and cos are available at the touch of a button on most hand-calculators.

Perhaps the most surprising aspect of this is that all these functions are computed in most hand-calculators by minor variations of the same algorithm. The so-called **CORDIC** (COordinate Rotation DIgital Computer) **algorithms** were first developed by Volder for solving trigonometric problems in in-flight navigation systems. (In mathematics, it is usual that methods or theorems bear the names of their discoverers and so perhaps these should properly be termed Volder methods. The use of the name CORDIC is a testament to their having been discovered by an engineer.)

Before discussing the algorithms in detail, it is worth pointing out some of the different requirements of routines for use in hand-calculators and those for digital computers. Firstly, a computer will use binary (or perhaps octal or hexadecimal) arithmetic throughout but this is not sensible within a calculator where the result of each step in the computation is displayed in conventional decimal form. The conversions between the two representations for every operation would be far too time consuming. Calculator algorithms must therefore be able to work with decimal arithmetic.

This requirement of decimal arithmetic has further implications. Long multiplication of binary numbers is straightforward as it consists solely of shifts and additions. In decimal notation, we need a one-digit multiplication table and the ability to handle fairly complicated carries as well as the shifts and additions. For example 73×47 as a decimal calculation requires four single-digit products involving two carries and then an addition involving one further carry. In binary

$$73 \times 47 = 1001001$$
$$\times\ 101111$$

$$
\begin{array}{l}
1001001 \\
1001001 \\
1001001 \\
1001001 \\
1001001
\end{array}
$$

Each of these terms is just
$$1001001$$
shifted the appropriate number of places.

$$110101100111$$

One of the primary aims of the CORDIC algorithms was to achieve this kind of simplicity for the elementary functions using *decimal* arithmetic.

The other essential difference caused by the use of decimal arithmetic is that, because multiplication and division are more complicated, the use of the defining power series, for, say, exp or cos is inappropriate whereas, with sensible initial scaling, such series can form the basis of computer routines.

The CORDIC algorithms are all based on an ingenious decomposition of the required answer in terms of simple constants so that only additions and exponent shifts are needed. The following theorem lies at the heart of the matter.

THEOREM 4.5.1   Suppose that the numbers σ_k, $k = 0, 1, \ldots, n$, are decreasing and positive and that

$$\sigma_k \leqslant \sum_{j=k+1}^{n} \sigma_j + \sigma_n. \qquad (4.28)$$

Suppose too that

$$|r| \leqslant \sum_{j=0}^{n} \sigma_j + \sigma_n.$$

Then the sequence defined by $s_0 = 0$, $s_{k+1} = s_k + \delta_k \sigma_k$, $k = 0, 1, \ldots, n$, where $\delta_k = \text{sgn}(r - s_k)$ and $\text{sgn } 0 = 1$ satisfies, for each k,

$$|r - s_k| \leqslant \sum_{j=k}^{n} \sigma_j + \sigma_n.$$

In particular, s_{n+1} approximates r with an error bounded by σ_n, that is,

$$|r - s_{n+1}| \leqslant \sigma_n.$$

(Note that sgn is the usual **signum** function: $\text{sgn } x = 1$ if $x \geqslant 0$; $\text{sgn } x = -1$ if $x < 0$.)

Proof   We use a simple induction argument. For $k = 0$, we have

$$|r - s_0| = |r|$$

$$\leqslant \sum_{j=0}^{n} \sigma_j + \sigma_n.$$

Now, assuming the result for some value of k and noting that δ_k is chosen to have the same sign as $r - s_k$, we obtain

$$|r - s_{k+1}| = |r - s_k - \delta_k \sigma_k|$$
$$= ||r - s_k| - \sigma_k|.$$

Then, by equation (4.28) and the induction hypothesis, we deduce that

$$-\left(\sum_{j=k+1}^{n} \sigma_j + \sigma_n \right) \leqslant -\sigma_k$$

$$\leqslant |r - s_k| - \sigma_k$$

$$\leqslant \sum_{j=k}^{n} \sigma_j + \sigma_n - \sigma_k$$

$$= \sum_{j=k+1}^{n} \sigma_j + \sigma_n$$

as required.

This theorem shows that, if we choose a sequence $\sigma_0, \sigma_1, \ldots, \sigma_n$ to satisfy these conditions, then we can write any number in the interval $[-E, E]$ where $E = \sum_{j=0}^{n} \sigma_j + \sigma_n$ in the form $\pm\sigma_0 \pm \sigma_1 \pm \ldots \pm \sigma_n$ with an error no worse than σ_n.

Example 4.5.1

The values $\sigma_k = 2^{-k}$ satisfy the conditions of the theorem, and so for any $r \in [-2, 2]$, we can write $r \approx \pm 1 \pm \frac{1}{2} \pm \frac{1}{4} \pm \frac{1}{8} \pm \ldots \pm 2^{-n}$ with an error less than 2^{-n}. For example, with $r = 1.2345$ and $n = 4$, we get

$\delta_0 = +1$	$s_1 = 0 + 1 = 1.0$	$\lvert r - s_1 \rvert = 0.2345 \leqslant 1,$
$\delta_1 = +1$	$s_2 = 1.0 + 0.5 = 1.5$	$\lvert r - s_2 \rvert = 0.2655 \leqslant 0.5,$
$\delta_2 = -1$	$s_3 = 1.5 - 0.25 = 1.25$	$\lvert r - s_3 \rvert = 0.0155 \leqslant 0.25,$
$\delta_3 = -1$	$s_4 = 1.25 - 0.125 = 1.125$	$\lvert r - s_4 \rvert = 0.1095 \leqslant 0.125,$
$\delta_4 = +1$	$s_5 = 1.125 + 0.0625 = 1.1875$	$\lvert r - s_5 \rvert = 0.0470 \leqslant 0.0625.$

Clearly, this could be continued to any accuracy.

It was emphasised in introducing the CORDIC algorithms that we wish to be able to compute directly with the decimal representation. Now taking $\sigma_k = 10^{-k}$ does not satisfy equation (4.28) but, if each step is repeated nine times so that

$$\sigma_{9k+j} = 10^{-k} \qquad \text{for } j = 0, 1, \ldots, 8 \text{ and } k = 0, 1, \ldots,$$

then this condition is indeed satisfied. With the same $r = 1.2345$, we then obtain

$$\delta_0 = \delta_1 = +1, \delta_2 = -1, \delta_3 = +1, \ldots, \delta_8 = -1 \qquad \text{with } \sigma_{0+j} = 1$$

so that

$$s_9 = 1.0,$$
$$\lvert r - s_9 \rvert = 0.2345 \leqslant 1.$$

Similarly, we have

$$\delta_9 = \delta_{10} = \delta_{11} = +1, \delta_{12} = -1, \delta_{13} = +1, \ldots, \delta_{17} = +1 \qquad \text{with } \sigma_{9+j} = 0.1$$

so that

$$s_{18} = 1.3,$$
$$\lvert r - s_{18} \rvert = 0.0655 \leqslant 0.1,$$

and also

$$\delta_{18} = \delta_{19} = \ldots = \delta_{24} = -1, \delta_{25} = +1, \delta_{26} = -1 \qquad \text{with } \sigma_{18+j} = 0.01$$

so that

$$s_{27} = 1.23,$$

$$|r - s_{27}| = 0.0045 \leqslant 0.01.$$

Again the process can be continued to any accuracy.

Despite the emphasis on the need for decimal calculation, we shall consider for the rest of this section only the binary forms of the CORDIC algorithms. The corresponding decimal forms can be obtained in precisely the same sort of way as in the above example. The following general algorithm, with appropriate choices for the parameters m and σ_k, yields approximations to a wide class of elementary functions.

General CORDIC algorithm (binary version)

From appropriately chosen starting values x_0, y_0, z_0, generate three sequences by

$$x_{k+1} = x_k - m\delta_k y_k 2^{-k} \qquad (4.29a)$$

$$y_{k+1} = y_k + \delta_k x_k 2^{-k} \qquad (4.29b)$$

$$z_{k+1} = z_k - \delta_k \sigma_k \qquad (4.29c)$$

Here m takes one of the values -1, 0 or 1 and is fixed for any particular application. Thus these operations consist only of (binary) exponent shifts and additions.

The choice of the signs δ_k can be made in one of two ways which again is fixed for any particular case:

(a) $\delta_k = \operatorname{sgn}(z_k)$, which is the **rotation mode**;

(b) $\delta_k = -\operatorname{sgn}(y_k)$, which is the **vectoring mode**.

(These names are a historical accident due to the development of the algorithms for navigational purposes. They are not of great value in understanding the methods.)

Examples 4.5.2

1 *Division* Here we use $m = 0$ in the vectoring mode with $\sigma_k = 2^{-k}$. Choosing $z_0 = 0$, we find that $|z_{n+1} - y_0/x_0| < 2^{-n}$. To see this, note first

that, since $m = 0$, $x_k = x_0$ for every k and so the process reduces to just the two equations

$$y_{k+1} = y_k + \delta_k x_0 2^{-k}$$

and

$$z_{k+1} = z_k - \delta_k 2^{-k}.$$

The choice of δ_k is such that in equation (4.29b) we decompose y_0 as $-\sum_{k=0}^{n} \delta_k x_0 2^{-k}$ or, equivalently, we have

$$\frac{y_0}{x_0} \approx -\sum_{k=0}^{n} \delta_k 2^{-k}$$

with an error bounded by 2^{-n}. However, in equation (4.29c) with $z_0 = 0$, we see that $z_{n+1} = -\Sigma \delta_k 2^{-k}$.

Consider, for example, $1.2/2.3$. Then

$$y_0 = 1.2, \qquad x_0 = 2.3, \qquad z_0 = 0 \qquad \delta_0 = -\operatorname{sgn}(y_0) = -1.$$

So

$$y_1 = 1.2 - 2.3 \times 2^0 \qquad z_1 = 0 - (-1) \times 2^0$$

$$= -1.1 \qquad\qquad = 1 \qquad\qquad\qquad \delta_1 = +1,$$

$$y_2 = -1.1 + 2.3 \times 2^{-1} \qquad z_2 = 1 - 2^{-1}$$

$$= 0.05 \qquad\qquad = 0.5 \qquad\qquad\qquad \delta_2 = -1,$$

$$y_3 = 0.05 - \frac{2.3}{4} \qquad z_3 = 0.5 + \frac{1}{4}$$

$$= -0.525 \qquad\qquad = 0.75 \qquad\qquad\qquad \delta_3 = +1,$$

$$y_4 = -0.525 + 0.2875 \qquad z_4 = 0.75 - 0.125$$

$$= -0.2375 \qquad\qquad = 0.625 \qquad\qquad\qquad \delta_4 = +1,$$

$$y_5 = -0.093\,75 \qquad\qquad z_5 = 0.5625 \qquad\qquad\qquad \delta_5 = +1,$$

$$y_6 = -0.021\,875 \qquad\qquad z_6 = 0.531\,25 \qquad\qquad\qquad \dots\dots\dots$$

We see that the values of y_k are being driven towards 0 by the choice of the signs and that the values of z_k are approaching $1.2/2.3 = 0.521\,74$ to five decimal places, and indeed the error in z_6 is about 0.01 which is less than $2^{-5} = 0.031\,25$.

Multiplication is achieved by the same algorithm in rotation mode; taking $y_0 = 0$ we obtain $y_{n+1} \approx x_0 z_0$ with an error of less than $x_0 \times 2^{-n}$.

2 *Trigonometric functions* For these we use $m = 1$ and take $\sigma_k = \tan^{-1}(2^{-k})$.

(The fact that this sequence of numbers satisfies the conditions of the theorem can be established by an application of the mean-value theorem.)

The rotation mode provides a method of computing $\sin \theta$ and $\cos \theta$ by setting $z_0 = \theta$ and decomposing z_0 as $\Sigma \delta_k \sigma_k$. Then writing $s_k = \theta - z_k$, it follows from equation (4.29c) that $s_{k+1} = s_k + \delta_k \sigma_k$ and so

$$\cos (s_{k+1}) = \cos(s_k + \delta_k \sigma_k)$$
$$= \cos (s_k) \cos (\delta_k \sigma_k) - \sin (s_k) \sin (\delta_k \sigma_k)$$

and

$$\sin (s_{k+1}) = \sin (s_k + \delta_k \sigma_k)$$
$$= \sin (s_k) \cos (\delta_k \sigma_k) + \cos (s_k) \sin (\delta_k \sigma_k).$$

Dividing these two equations by $\cos (\sigma_k)$ and using $\tan (\sigma_k) = 2^{-k}$, we get

$$\frac{\cos (s_{k+1})}{\cos (\sigma_k)} = \cos (s_k) - \delta_k 2^{-k} \sin (s_k) \tag{4.30a}$$

and

$$\frac{\sin (s_{k+1})}{\cos (\sigma_k)} = \sin (s_k) - \delta_k 2^{-k} \cos (s_k). \tag{4.30b}$$

From Theorem 4.5.1, it follows that $|z_{n+1}| = |s_{n+1} - \theta| \leqslant \sigma_n$ and the repeated application of these identities shows that taking

$$x_0 = \prod_{k=0}^{n} \cos(\sigma_k) = K, \quad \text{say, and} \quad y_0 = 0 \quad \text{then gives} \quad x_{n+1} \approx \cos \theta \quad \text{and}$$
$y_{n+1} \approx \sin \theta$ each with an error bounded by 2^{-n}.

In the vectoring mode with $z_0 = 0$, we obtain

$$z_{n+1} \approx \tan^{-1} \left(\frac{y_0}{x_0} \right)$$

and

$$x_{n+1} \approx K \sqrt{x_0^2 + y_0^2}.$$

The CORDIC schemes for the trigonometric functions require the storage of the constants σ_k and K. For example, we estimate the value $\cos 1$ using $n = 4$. Now $\sigma_0 = \tan^{-1} 1 = 0.7854$, $\sigma_1 = \tan^{-1} (\tfrac{1}{2}) = 0.4636$, $\sigma_2 = 0.2450$, $\sigma_3 = 0.1244$ and $K = \cos (0.7854) \cos (0.4636) \cos (0.2450) \cos (0.1244) = 0.6088$. Thence we get

$x_0 = 0.6088$	$y_0 = 0.0000$	$z_0 = 1.0000$	$\delta_0 = +1,$
$x_1 = 0.6088$	$y_1 = 0.6088$	$z_1 = 0.2146$	$\delta_1 = +1,$
$x_2 = 0.3044$	$y_2 = 0.9132$	$z_2 = -0.2490$	$\delta_2 = -1,$

$$x_3 = 0.5327 \qquad y_3 = 0.8371 \qquad z_3 = -0.0040 \qquad \delta_3 = -1,$$

$$x_4 = 0.6373 \qquad y_4 = 0.7705 \qquad z_4 = 0.1204 \qquad \delta_4 = +1,$$

and so $\cos 1 \approx x_5 = 0.5891$ and $\sin 1 \approx y_5 = 0.8103$ which are both in error by less than $2^{-4} = 0.0625$ since the true values are 0.5403 and 0.8415, respectively.

Note that as in the case of the division algorithm the errors are not necessarily reduced at each stage of the computation. The compensatory advantage is that we do know in *advance* the number of steps of the algorithm that are needed to achieve any specified accuracy.

3 *Hyperbolic and exponential functions* The algorithms for these functions are very similar to those for the trigonometric functions above. This time we take $m = -1$, $\sigma_k = \tanh^{-1}(2^{-k})$ for $k \geqslant 1$ and use the corresponding identities for the hyperbolic functions to derive equations similar to equations (4.30). There is an important difference, however. The quantities σ_k just given *do not* fulfil the conditions of the theorem; in particular, equation (4.28) is not satisfied. It can be shown, however, that, if the steps for $k = 4, 13, 40, \ldots$ (or, in general, $k = (3^n - 1)/2$ for $n = 2, 3, \ldots$) are repeated, then all the conditions are satisfied. This time therefore we take $K = \Pi \cosh(\sigma_k)$ where the factors corresponding to the repetitions are of course also repeated.

In the rotation mode, we then find that, if $x_1 = K$ and $y_1 = 0$, then $x_{n+1} \approx \cosh(z_1)$ and $y_{n+1} \approx \sinh(z_1)$. From these, we can obtain $\exp(\pm z_1)$ and $\tanh(z_1)$.

With $z_1 = 0$, the vectoring mode can be used to obtain

$$z_{n+1} \approx \tanh^{-1}\left(\frac{y_1}{x_1}\right)$$

$$= \frac{\ln w}{2},$$

where $x_1 = w + 1$ and $y_1 = w - 1$, and

$$x_{n+1} \approx K\sqrt{x_1^2 - y_1^2}$$

$$= K\sqrt{w},$$

where $x_1 = w + \frac{1}{4}$ and $y_1 = w - \frac{1}{4}$.

We illustrate the use of these algorithms by estimating the value $\exp(0.2)$ using $n = 5$. Firstly, with $m = -1$, equations (4.29a) and (4.29b) become

$$x_{k+1} = x_k + \delta_k y_k 2^{-k}$$

and

$$y_{k+1} = y_k + \delta_k x_k 2^{-k}.$$

Writing $u_k = x_k + y_k$, we thus have

$$u_{k+1} = u_k + \delta_k u_k 2^{-k}. \tag{4.31}$$

Now $\sigma_1 = \tanh^{-1}(\tfrac{1}{2}) = 0.5493$, $\sigma_2 = \tanh^{-1}(\tfrac{1}{4}) = 0.2554$, $\sigma_3 = 0.1257$ and $\sigma_4 = 0.0626$ and so, allowing for the repetition of σ_4,

$$K = \cosh(0.5493)\cosh(0.2554)\cosh(0.1257)\cosh(0.0626)\cosh(0.626)$$

$$= 1.2067.$$

Then

$u_1 = 1.2067$	$z_1 = 0.2000$	$\delta_1 = +1,$
$u_2 = 1.8101$	$z_2 = -0.3493$	$\delta_2 = -1,$
$u_3 = 1.3576$	$z_3 = -0.0939$	$\delta_3 = -1,$
$u_4 = 1.1879$	$z_4 = 0.0318$	$\delta_4 = +1,$
$u_5 = 1.2621$	$z_5 = -0.0308$	$\delta_5 = -1,$
$u_5 = 1.1832$	$z_5 = 0.0318$	$\delta_5 = +1,$

and so $\exp(0.2) \approx u_6 = 1.2202$ which compares with the true value 1.2214.

In the above examples, no notice was taken of the final condition of Theorem 4.5.1, namely that

$$|r| \leqslant \sum_{j=0}^{n} \sigma_j + \sigma_n.$$

In the case of division this imposes the requirement $|y_0/x_0| \leqslant 2$ which is always satisfied by the fractional parts of normalised floating-point binary numbers. Similarly we find that this condition causes no difficulty for floating-point multiplication and, because of the repetitions, this is also true for the decimal operations.

For the trigonometric functions, we find that

$$\sigma_0 + \sigma_1 + \sigma_2 + \sigma_3 = \tan^{-1}1 + \tan^{-1}(\tfrac{1}{2}) + \tan^{-1}(\tfrac{1}{4}) + \tan^{-1}(\tfrac{1}{8})$$

$$\approx 1.6184$$

$$> \frac{\pi}{2};$$

so the range $-\pi/2 \leqslant \theta \leqslant \pi/2$ is covered and extension of the sine and cosine functions is therefore straightforward. The identity $\tan^{-1}(1/y) = \pi/2 - \tan^{-1}y$ allows us to restrict the arctangent routine to the use of $x_0 = 1$ and $|y_0| < 1$ to cover the complete range.

For the exponential and hyperbolic functions, this problem of extending the range is less straightforward and is handled in very different ways in different situations. One convenient technique for use with the binary CORDIC algorithm for the exponential function is to write

$$z = z_0 + p \ln 2,$$

where p is an integer chosen so that $z_0 \in [0, \ln 2)$. Then z_0 is within the range of applicability of the algorithm and

$$\exp z = \exp(p \ln 2) \exp(z_0)$$
$$= 2^p \exp(z_0)$$

The error in the value of $\exp(z_0)$ will be bounded by 2^{-n+1} where n is the number of steps used in the CORDIC algorithm. It is thus easy to determine in advance the number of such steps that are needed for any particular floating-point format and this number remains constant for all arguments z.

It is necessary here to give a word of warning about the possibility of meaningless computation. Suppose that a calculator works to seven decimal digits so that a number A is represented by $a \times 10^\alpha$ with $1 \leqslant a < 10$. The difference between A and the next representable number is then $10^{\alpha-6}$ which is certainly greater than 2π whenever $\alpha \geqslant 7$. To try to give a value of, say, $\cos A$ is then plainly meaningless as more than one complete period of the cosine function would have this same representation. Nonetheless many calculators and computers would attribute a definite value for $\cos A$ which emphasises the point that any output from a computer or calculator should be treated with suspicion until the method has been analysed carefully.

Before leaving the subject of approximate evaluation of functions, it should be stressed that, although many practical algorithms will be based on the use of one or more of these, the methods and approaches discussed here are by no means the only ones available. The routines used in digital computers for the elementary functions provide ample testimony to the variety and blend of approaches which can be useful in different circumstances.

EXERCISES 4.5

1 Prove that $\sigma_k = 2^{-k}$, $k = 0, 1, \ldots, n$, satisfy equation (4.28). Use the CORDIC algorithm to find 1.23×1.12 with an error less than 2^{-7}.

2 Show that $\sigma_k = \tan^{-1}(2^{-k})$, $k = 0, 1, \ldots, n$, satisfy the conditions of Theorem 4.5.1. Find $\tan(0.5)$ using the CORDIC algorithm with $n = 5$.

3 Derive a simplified CORDIC scheme, similar to that using equation (4.31), for finding $\exp(-z)$. Use this algorithm to find $\exp(-0.25)$ with $n = 6$.

4 Use the CORDIC algorithm to find $\ln(1.5)$ using $n = 6$.

5 NUMERICAL CALCULUS

5.1 INTRODUCTION

In the last few chapters, we have seen the need for numerical techniques for the evaluation of functions and have discussed a variety of approaches to the problem. However, the evaluation of a function is only the beginning; many other questions arise in order that we should understand the nature of any particular function. So here we wish to find numerical answers to those same questions.

In this chapter, we consider some of the methods of numerical calculus— that is, numerical integration and differentiation—and then the finding of turning points. The techniques which we deal with here are, for the most part, derived from the ideas of interpolation. Thus the basic numerical integration formulae which we consider can be obtained by integrating interpolation polynomials. It is with this topic that we begin.

5.2 NUMERICAL INTEGRATION

We have already seen some examples of integrals which cannot be performed exactly, and one approach to the approximate evaluation of such integrals by expressing the integrand as a power series. In this section, we introduce the ideas of numerical integration in which we approximate $\int_a^b f(x)\,dx$ by a weighted sum of values of the function f at some finite set of points. That is, we use approximations of the form

$$\int_a^b f(x)\,dx \approx \sum_{j=0}^{n} c_j f(x_j). \tag{5.1}$$

115

The aim of a good numerical integration algorithm is that such a formula should be both simple and efficient—and, of course, it should give good approximations to the true integrals. These methods are based on integrating a polynomial which has the same value as f at a set of points $x_0, x_1, \ldots, x_n$—that is, an interpolation polynomial.

The fact that such an integration formula is derived from integrating the interpolation polynomial also provides us with a method for finding the **weights** c_j in equation (5.1). Let p be the interpolation polynomial agreeing with f at $x_0, x_1, \ldots, x_n$. Then the corresponding **interpolatory quadrature** or **numerical integration rule** is given by

$$\int_a^b f(x)\,\mathrm{d}x \approx \int_a^b p(x)\,\mathrm{d}x$$

$$= \int_a^b \sum_{j=0}^n f(x_j)l_j(x)\,\mathrm{d}x$$

$$= \sum_{j=0}^n c_j f(x_j), \qquad (5.2)$$

where the $l_j(x)$ are the Lagrange basis polynomials which we met in the previous chapter. From this, it follows that

$$c_j = \int_a^b l_j(x)\,\mathrm{d}x \qquad j = 0, 1, \ldots, n. \qquad (5.3)$$

Now, if the integrand f were itself a polynomial of degree not more than n, then the interpolation polynomial agreeing with f at these points would be f itself and so integrating this interpolation polynomial would yield the exact integral. This consideration leads to the following definition.

DEFINITION 5.2.1   The numerical integration formula (5.1) has **degree of precision** m if it is exact for all polynomials of degree at most m but not for x^{m+1}.

Any *interpolatory* quadrature rule using the **nodes** $x_0, x_1, \ldots, x_n$ must therefore have degree of precision *at least* n. (We shall see later that the degree of precision of such a formula can be greater than n.) This observation provides us with a more amenable technique for obtaining the quadrature weights than that given by equation (5.3).

Example 5.2.1

Find the interpolatory quadrature rule using the points $x_0 = 0$, $x_1 = 1$ and $x_2 = 3$ for evaluating

$$I = \int_0^4 f(x)\,dx.$$

Since the formula must have degree of precision at least 2, we seek weights c_0, c_1 and c_2 such that

$$I = \int_0^4 f(x)\,dx$$

$$\approx c_0 f(0) + c_1 f(1) + c_2 f(3)$$

is exact for $f(x) = 1,\ x,\ x_2$. Now with

$f(x) = 1 \qquad I = 4 \ $ and $\ c_0 f(0) + c_1 f(1) + c_2 f(3) = c_0 + c_1 + c_2,$

$f(x) = x \qquad I = 8 \ $ and $\ c_0 f(0) + c_1 f(1) + c_2 f(3) = c_1 + 3c_2,$

$f(x) = x^2 \qquad I = \frac{64}{3} \ $ and $\ c_0 f(0) + c_1 f(1) + c_2 f(3) = c_1 + 9c_2.$

The equations

$$c_0 + c_1 + c_2 = 4,$$

$$c_1 + 3c_2 = 8,$$

$$c_1 + 9c_2 = \tfrac{64}{3}$$

have the solution

$$c_0 = \tfrac{4}{9},$$

$$c_1 = \tfrac{4}{3},$$

$$c_2 = \tfrac{20}{9}$$

and so the required quadrature rule is

$$I = \int_0^4 f(x)\,dx$$

$$\approx \frac{4[f(0) + 3f(1) + 5f(3)]}{9}.$$

With $f(x) = x^3$, we have $I = 4^4/4 = 64$ while the integration formula yields $552/3$ which has a relative error of about 4%. In this particular case, we

117

thus see that the degree of precision is the same as the degree of the interpolating polynomial.

Fortunately, it is not untypical of numerical integration that small relative errors can be obtained from simple approaches. Clearly though the distribution of the nodes will affect the accuracy that can be obtained. In the above example there is only one of them in the right-hand three-quarters of the range of integration.

In the above example, we set out to find a quadrature rule which has degree of precision at least 2 and the procedure was to find the weights so that the rule is exact for 1, x and x^2. The fact that this is sufficient to establish exactness for all quadratics follows readily from the **linearity** of both the integral and the numerical integration formula. (Thus, for any quadratic polynomial $p(x) = ax^2 + bx + c$, we see that

$$\int p(x)\, dx = a \int x^2 \, dx + b \int x \, dx + c \int 1 \, dx,$$

and a similar result holds for the quadrature rule.)

It is clear that, following the approach used in the above example, we can find the interpolatory quadrature rule corresponding to any set of nodes by solving a system of linear equations. We shall concentrate here on just three elementary integration formulae: the **midpoint rule**

$$\int_a^b f(x)\, dx \approx (b-a) f\left(\frac{a+b}{2}\right), \tag{5.4}$$

the **trapezium rule**

$$\int_a^b f(x)\, dx \approx \frac{b-a}{2}[f(a) + f(b)] \tag{5.5}$$

and **Simpson's rule**

$$\int_a^b f(x)\, dx \approx \frac{b-a}{6}\left[f(a) + 4f\left(\frac{a+b}{2}\right) + f(b)\right]. \tag{5.6}$$

These are obtained by integrating the polynomials of degrees 0, 1 and 2, respectively, which agree with the f at the given integration points. We illustrate the derivation with the special case of Simpson's rule for the interval $[-h, h]$.

We require an integration rule which uses the values $f(-h)$, $f(0)$ and $f(h)$ and yields the exact result for all quadratics. Therefore we must find α, β and γ such that

$$I = \int_{-h}^{h} f(x)\,dx$$

$$= \alpha f(-h) + \beta f(0) + \gamma f(h)$$

for $f(x) = 1$, x and x^2. We thus obtain the following equations:

$$f(x) = 1; \quad I = 2h = \alpha + \beta + \gamma$$

$$f(x) = x; \quad I = 0 = -\alpha h + \gamma h$$

$$f(x) = x^2; \quad I = \frac{2h^3}{3} = \alpha h^2 + \gamma h^2.$$

From the last two of these we get $\alpha = \gamma = h/3$ and then $\beta = 2h - 2h/3 = 4h/3$.

We can obtain the corresponding formula for the general interval $[a, b]$ using the simple change of variables

$$x = \frac{a+b}{2} + s \qquad \text{with} \qquad h = \frac{b-a}{2}.$$

This yields

$$\int_{a}^{b} f(x)\,dx = \int_{-h}^{h} f\left(\frac{a+b}{2} + s\right) ds$$

$$\approx \frac{h}{3}\left[f\left(\frac{a+b}{2} - h\right) + 4f\left(\frac{a+b}{2}\right) + f\left(\frac{a+b}{2} + h\right)\right]$$

$$= \frac{h}{3}[f(a) + 4f(a+h) + f(b)]$$

as in equation (5.6).

Now we remarked earlier that it is possible for a quadrature rule to have a higher degree of precision than that of the interpolation polynomial. In the case of Simpson's rule, we find that

$$\int_{-h}^{h} x^3\,dx = 0$$

$$= \frac{h}{3}[(-h)^3 + 4(0)^3 + (h)^3].$$

That is, Simpson's rule is exact for cubics and so has degree of precision 3. (It is not exact for x^4.) The midpoint rule yields a similar bonus since it has degree of precision 1.

119

Of course the performance of these formulae for low-degree polynomials is not our only concern and we need to get some idea of how good (or bad) the approximate integrals will be. Error formulae for interpolatory quadrature rules can be obtained by the integration of the remainder term for polynomial interpolation. In very few cases is this process other than extremely messy and we shall omit the details altogether. However, for the three formulae given earlier, we get

$$\int_a^b f(x)\,dx - (b-a)f\left(\frac{a+b}{2}\right) = \frac{(b-a)h^2 f''(\theta_1)}{6}, \tag{5.7}$$

where $h = (b-a)/2$,

$$\int_a^b f(x)\,dx - \frac{b-a}{2}[f(a)+f(b)] = -(b-a)h^2 f''(\theta_2), \tag{5.8}$$

where $h = b-a$, and

$$\int_a^b f(x)\,dx - \frac{h}{3}[f(a)+4f(a+h)+f(b)] = \frac{-(b-a)h^4 f^{(4)}(\theta_3)}{180}, \tag{5.9}$$

where $h = (b-a)/2$. (Here $\theta_1, \theta_2, \theta_3$ are 'mean-value points' in the interval (a,b).

Example 5.2.2

Estimate

$$I = \frac{1}{\sqrt{2\pi}} \int_0^{0.5} \exp\left(-\frac{x^2}{2}\right) dx.$$

(a) By the midpoint rule, we find that

$$I \approx \frac{0.5\exp(-0.25^2/2)}{\sqrt{2\pi}}$$

$$= 0.193\,33.$$

(b) Using the trapezium rule, we get

$$I \approx \frac{0.25[\exp 0 + \exp(-0.5^2/2)]}{\sqrt{2\pi}}$$

$$= 0.187\,75.$$

(c) Simpson's rule gives

$$I \approx \frac{0.25[\exp 0 + 4\exp(-0.25^2/2) + \exp(-0.5^2/2)]}{3\sqrt{2\pi}}$$

$$= 0.191\,47.$$

From the power series estimate used in section 3.5, we obtain $I = 0.191\,462\,4$ using just five terms, giving an error of less than 5×10^{-9}.

Clearly the trapezium rule estimate (or any other) could be improved by use of the fact that

$$\int_0^{0.5} f(x)\,dx = \int_0^{0.25} f(x)\,dx + \int_{0.25}^{0.5} f(x)\,dx.$$

For the above example, this yields the estimate $I \approx 0.190\,54$.

This process of subdividing the range of integration and applying a basic rule to each subinterval can be continued indefinitely to provide a sequence of estimates which, for a continuous function, converges to the true value of the integral. Such an approach leads to the **composite integration formulae**.

Suppose then that we wish to evaluate the integral

$$I = \int_0^1 f(x)\,dx \tag{5.10}$$

and that the interval $[0, 1]$ is subdivided into N equal subintervals. Each has width $1/N$ and we denote the points j/N, $j = 0, 1, \ldots, N$, by x_j. The composite trapezium rule gives us the estimate

$$I \approx T_N$$
$$= \frac{f(x_0) + 2f(x_1) + 2f(x_2) + \ldots + 2f(x_{N-1}) + f(x_N)}{2N}. \tag{5.11}$$

Applying the composite midpoint rule to this same subdivision, we use the integration points $y_j = (x_j + x_{j-1})/2, j = 1, 2, \ldots, N)$, to get the estimate

$$I \approx M_N$$
$$= \frac{f(y_1) + f(y_2) + \ldots + f(y_N)}{N}. \tag{5.12}$$

The distribution of these points in the interval $[0, 1]$ is illustrated in Fig. 5.1.

The composite Simpson's rule for this same subdivision of the interval uses all these points to yield the estimate

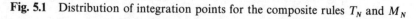

Fig. 5.1 Distribution of integration points for the composite rules T_N and M_N

$$S_N =$$

$$\frac{f(x_0) + 4f(y_1) + 2f(x_1) + 4f(y_2) + 2f(x_2) + \ldots + 2f(x_{N-1}) + 4f(y_N) + f(x_N)}{2N \times 3}$$

$$(5.13)$$

from which we see that

$$I \approx S_N$$

$$= \frac{T_N + 2M_N}{3}. \qquad (5.14)$$

This leads to a simple scheme for computing successive estimates of I using the sequences T_{2^n} and S_{2^n}.

If the intervals used for equations (5.11) are all halved, then the new trapezium rule estimate of I is just

$$T_{2N} = \frac{f(x_0) + 2f(y_1) + 2f(x_1) + 2f(y_2) + 2f(x_2) + \ldots + 2f(x_{N-1}) + 2f(y_N) + f(x_N)}{4N}$$

from which we deduce that

$$T_{2N} = \frac{T_N + M_N}{2} \qquad (5.15)$$

and hence, using equation (5.14), it follows that $S_{2N} = (T_{2N} + 2M_{2N})/3$ so that the only *new* computation required is that of M_{2N}.

Thus we have a straightforward procedure for finding successive members of the above sequences:

$$S_1 = \frac{T_1 + 2M_1}{3}$$

and then, for $n = 1, 2, \ldots,$

$$T_{2^n} = \frac{T_{2^{n-1}} + M_{2^{n-1}}}{2}$$

and

$$S_{2^n} = \frac{T_{2^n} + 2M_{2^n}}{3}$$

The new information required is just

$$M_{2^n} = \frac{1}{2^n} \sum_{i=1}^{2^n} f\left(\frac{2i-1}{2^{n+1}}\right).$$

Example 5.2.3

Evaluate

$$I = \frac{1}{\sqrt{2\pi}} \int_0^2 \exp\left(-\frac{x^2}{2}\right) dx.$$

Here, of course, the step lengths are all double those of the above development and so

$$M_1 = \frac{\exp(-\frac{1}{2})}{\sqrt{2\pi}}$$

$$= 0.483\,94$$

and

$$T_1 = \frac{\exp 0 + \exp(-2)}{\sqrt{2\pi}}$$

$$= 0.452\,93.$$

Hence

$$S_1 = \frac{0.452\,93 + 2 \times 0.483\,94}{3}$$

$$= 0.473\,61$$

and

$$T_2 = \frac{0.452\,93 + 0.483\,94}{2}$$

$$= 0.468\,44.$$

Next

$$M_2 = f(\tfrac{1}{2}) + f(\tfrac{3}{2})$$

$$= \frac{\exp(-\frac{1}{8}) + \exp(-\frac{9}{8})}{\sqrt{2\pi}}$$

$$= 0.481\,58,$$

so that

$$S_2 = 0.477\,20$$

and

$$T_4 = 0.475\,01.$$

Continuing the process, we get

$$M_4 = \frac{f(\tfrac{1}{4}) + f(\tfrac{3}{4}) + f(\tfrac{5}{4}) + f(\tfrac{7}{4})}{2}$$

$$= 0.478\,37,$$

$$S_4 = 0.477\,25,$$

$$T_8 = 0.476\,69,$$

$$M_8 = 0.477\,53$$

and so

$$S_8 = 0.477\,25$$

$$= S_4 \text{ to five decimal places.}$$

We have used a total of 17 function evaluations. (To obtain similar accuracy with the power series would require 11 terms.)

This procedure is implemented in the following program.

PROGRAM 5.2.1

```
1  REM******APPROXIMATE EVALUATION OF INTEGRALS BY******
   REM******          COMPOSITE SIMPSON'S RULE          ******
10 OPEN "RESULTS." FOR OUTPUT AS FILE £3
   PRINT £3, "EVALUATION OF INTEGRAL USING COMPOSITE SIMPSON'S RULE"
   PRINT £3, "F(X) = EXP( - X↑2/2)/SQR(2π)"
   PRINT £3, "RANGE OF INTEGRATION IS [0, 2]"
   PRINT £3, "TOLERANCE REQUIRED IS 1E - 6"
   DIMENSION M(10), T(10), S(10)
REM   M(N) IS VALUE OF MID-POINT RULE ESTIMATE USING 2↑N SUBINTERVALS
REM   T(N) IS VALUE OF TRAPEZIUM RULE ESTIMATE USING 2↑N SUBINTERVALS
REM   S(N) IS VALUE OF SIMPSON'S RULE ESTIMATE USING 2↑N SUBINTERVALS

20 A = 0 \ B = 2 \ E = 1E - 6
   DEF FNF(X) = EXP(-X↑2/2)/SQR(2*PI)
   N = 0 \ H = (B - A)/2 \ P = 1
   M(0) = 2*H*FNF(A + H) \ T(0) = H*(FNF(A) + FNF(B))
REM A, B ARE THE END-POINTS OF THE RANGE OF INTEGRATION AND
REM H IS STEPLENGTH FOR SIMPSON'S RULE, H1 IS THAT FOR MID-POINT RULE
REM P IS THE NUMBER OF POINTS TO BE USED BY THE MID-POINT RULE

30 FOR N = 0 TO 9
   S(N) = (T(N) + 2*M(N)/3
   PRINT £3, N: "M(";N;") = ";M(N),"T(";N;") = ";T(N),"S(";N;") = ";S(N)
   IF N > 1 THEN 31
       ELSE IF ABS(S(N) - S(N - 1)) < E/2 THEN 40
```

```
31    T(N + 1) = (T(N) + M(N))/2
      H1 = H \ H = H2 \ P = 2*P
      Y = A + H \ M(N + 1) = FNF(Y)
      FOR J = 1 TO P - 1
          Y = Y + H1 \ M(N + 1) = M(N + 1) + FNF(Y)
      NEXT J
      M(N + 1) = H1*M(N + 1)
      NEXT N
      S(10) = (T(10) + 2*M(10))/3
      PRINT £3, 10; "M(10) = "; M(10), "T(10) = "; T(10), "S(10) = "; S(10)
      PRINT £3, "FAILED TO ACHIEVE REQUIRED ACCURACY"
      GOTO 50

40    PRINT £3, "CONVERGED TO REQUIRED TOLERANCE"
50    STOP
      END
```

In the above process, we are continually halving the step length used over the whole range of integration. This may well be wasteful as on some parts of the interval we may obtain the required accuracy much more rapidly than elsewhere. This leads to consideration of the so-called **adaptive integration algorithms**. It is also the case that, if continual halving of the step length is used, then we can obtain greater accuracy from the information gathered than is available from just the composite Simpson's rule. We include a brief discussion of these ideas in the next section. First, however, we have the following result on the error in using the composite Simpson's rule.

THEOREM 5.2.1 Suppose the integral $\int_a^b f(x)\, dx$ is estimated by Simpson's rule using N equal subdivisions of $[a, b]$ and that $f^{(4)}$ is continuous. Then the error in this approximation is given, for some $\theta \in (a, b)$, by $-(b-a)h^4 f^{(4)}(\theta)/180$ where $h = (b-a)/2N$.

Proof Let $x_j = a + j(b-a)/N = a + 2jh, j = 0, 1, \ldots, N$, be the end-points of the subdivisions. Then, by equation (5.9), we have

$$\int_{x_j}^{x_{j+1}} f(x)\, dx - \frac{h}{3}[f(x_j) + 4f(x_j + h) + f(x_{j+1})] = \frac{-(x_{j+1} - x_j)h^4 f^{(4)}(\theta_j)}{180}$$

for some $\theta_j \in (x_j, x_{j+1})$. Since $x_{j+1} - x_j = 2h$, it follows that the overall error $E(S_N)$ is given by

$$E(S_N) = -\frac{h^5}{90} \sum_{j=0}^{N-1} f^{(4)}(\theta_j).$$

Since $f^{(4)}$ is continuous, there exist bounds m, M such that

$$m \leqslant f^{(4)}(x) \leqslant M \qquad \text{for all } x \in [a, b]$$

125

and hence

$$Nm \leqslant \sum_{j=0}^{N-1} f^{(4)}(\theta_j) \leqslant NM.$$

By the intermediate-value theorem, it follows that there exists $\theta \in (a, b)$ such that

$$Nf^{(4)}(\theta) = \sum_{j=0}^{N-1} f^{(4)}(\theta_j).$$

Since $Nh = (b - a)/2$, we may conclude that

$$E(S_N) = \frac{-Nh^5 f^{(4)}(\theta)}{90}$$

$$= \frac{-(b-a)h^4 f^{(4)}(\theta)}{180},$$

as required.

One immediate consequence of this result is that, as N increases, the sequence (S_N) will converge to the true value of the integral since $h \to 0$ as $N \to \infty$. Furthermore, if we suppose that $f^{(4)}(x)$ does not vary too wildly over the interval $[a, b]$, then our process of continually halving the step length (or of doubling N) will yield a rapidly convergent sequence.

For the above example, we have $b - a = 2$ and for the final estimate $h = \frac{1}{8}$. For $f(x) = \exp(-x^2/2)$, $f^{(4)}(x) = (x^4 - 6x^2 + 3)f(x)$ and hence $|f^{(4)}(x)| \leqslant |f^{(4)}(0)| \leqslant 3$ from which we obtain the error bound $E \leqslant 6 \times (\frac{1}{8})^4/180 \approx 0.8 \times 10^{-5}$, which implies that the quoted result is in error by less than 1 in the final figure shown.

Similar results can be obtained for the other composite rules. Such bounds can be used to estimate, *in advance* of the calculation, the step length and therefore the number of integration points which will be needed.

Example 5.2.4

Consider the integral

$$I = \int_1^2 \frac{1}{x}\, dx$$

$$= \ln 2.$$

Now the corresponding result to Theorem 5.2.1 for the trapezium rule gives the error formula

$$E(T_N) = \frac{-(b-a)h^2 f''(\theta)}{12} \qquad (5.16)$$

where $h = (b-a)/N$. In this particular case we have $b-a=1$ and $f''(x) = 2/x^3$ so that $|f''(x)| \leqslant \frac{2}{3}$ and therefore

$$|E(T_N)| \leqslant \frac{h^2}{18}$$

$$= \frac{1}{18N^2}.$$

Thus, in order to obtain $\ln 2$ by this method with an error of less than 0.5×10^{-5}, we need N such that $1/18N^2 \leqslant 0.5 \times 10^{-5}$ or, equivalently, $N^2 \geqslant 200\,000/18$ which implies that $N \geqslant 106$. That is, at least 107 function evaluations will be needed.

Using Simpson's rule with N subdivisions—and therefore $2N + 1$ function evaluations—we have, since $|f^{(4)}(x)| = |24/x^5| \leqslant 24$,

$$|E(S_N)| \leqslant \frac{24h^4}{180}$$

$$= \frac{2h^4}{15}$$

where now $h = (b-a)/2N$. To obtain the same accuracy, we require $h^4 \leqslant 0.5 \times 10^{-5} \times 15/2 = 3.75 \times 10^{-5}$ which is satisfied for all $h \leqslant 0.078\,25$ and therefore for all $N > 6$. The required accuracy can therefore be achieved taking $N = 7$ and using just 15 integration points.

EXERCISES 5.2

1 Find the interpolatory quadrature rule for the interval $[-2, 2]$ using the nodes $-1, 0, 1, 2$. What is its degree of precision?

2 Estimate the value of $\ln 2$ using the integral of Example 5.2.4 using the basic midpoint, trapezium and Simpson's rules and then the composite rules using 2^n equal subdivisions of the interval for $n = 1, 2, 3$. Verify that in the last case the accuracy predicted by Example 5.2.4 for Simpson's rule is achieved.

3 Derive the error formula (5.16) for the composite trapezium rule. (Use a similar argument to that of Theorem 5.2.1.) Use this to estimate the error in the value of the final trapezium rule estimate of Exercises 5.2, **2**.

4 How many integration points would be needed to evaluate

$$I = \frac{1}{\sqrt{2\pi}} \int_0^2 \exp\left(-\frac{x^2}{2}\right) dx$$

with an error less than 10^{-7} using

(a) the trapezium rule and
(b) Simpson's rule?

5 Modify Program 5.2.1 to obtain $\ln 2$ with an error of less than 10^{-6}.

6 Modify Program 5.2.1 to evaluate

$$I = \int_0^1 \sqrt{x}\, dx$$

with successively greater accuracy requirements. Can you explain what is happening?

7 We observed that, if $f^{(4)}(x)$ is approximately constant over the range of integration, then the sequence of Simpson's rule estimates obtained by Program 5.2.1 should be rapidly convergent. Estimate the ratio $E(S_2)/E(S_1)$ in this situation. Suggest a better quadrature rule using the same five points as S_2.

5.3 PRACTICAL NUMERICAL INTEGRATION

In this section, we consider briefly some of the practical approaches to the problem of numerical integration.

In the previous section, we saw that good results can be obtained by using a low-order rule for a suitable subdivision of the interval. This observation leads to the development of *adaptive* quadrature schemes in which the important consideration is the manner in which the subdivision is obtained. Typically, a composite low-degree interpolatory formula such as Simpson's rule is then used within each subinterval to obtain the required accuracy there.

We also saw that we can build up more accurate formulae from suitable combinations of simpler ones. For example, Simpson's rule was obtained as a simple combination of the midpoint and trapezium rules using (some of) the same points. In Exercises 5.2, **7**, it was also suggested that a better formula could be obtained from two applications of Simpson's rule using three and five points. This basic idea can be extended to yield the **Romberg integration scheme**.

A third approach is suggested by the observation that the degree of precision of a quadrature formula can be higher than the degree of the corresponding interpolation polynomial. Thus it may be worthwhile to seek the quadrature rule of maximum possible degree using some fixed number of nodes. The general theory of this **Gaussian integration** approach is beyond the scope of the present text. However, we can get a taste of its rich theory through some examples.

Example 5.3.1

Find the interpolatory quadrature formulae of maximum possible degree of precision on the interval $[-1, 1]$ using

(a) two points and
(b) three points.

For simplicity of notation, we denote for the time being $\displaystyle\int_{-1}^{1} f(x)\, dx$ by $I(f)$.

(a) We must find the nodes x_0 and x_1 and the weights c_0 and c_1 to make the formula exact for $f(x) = 1, x, x^2, \ldots$ for as high a power as possible. Since there are four unknowns, it is reasonable to aim to satisfy four such equations. Note that $I(x^{2n}) = 2/(2n+1)$ while $I(x^{2n+1}) = 0$. Thus we require the following.

(i) For $f(x) = 1$, $I(f) = 2 = c_0 + c_1$.
(ii) For $f(x) = x$, $I(f) = 0 = c_0 x_0 + c_1 x_1$.
(iii) For $f(x) = x^2$, $I(f) = \frac{2}{3} = c_0 x_0^2 + c_1 x_1^2$.
(iv) For $f(x) = x^3$, $I(f) = 0 = c_0 x_0^3 + c_1 x_1^3$.

From (ii), we see that $c_0 x_0 = -c_1 x_1$ and substituting this in (iv) yields

$$0 = c_0 x_0^3 + c_1 x_1^3 = c_0 x_0 (x_0^2 - x_1^2).$$

Now $c_0 \neq 0$ since otherwise we would have just a one-point formula and similarly we could deduce from $x_0 = 0$ that either $x_1 = 0$ also or $c_1 = 0$ which again would imply that we have just a one-point formula. Thus it follows that $x_0^2 = x_1^2$ and therefore that $x_0 = -x_1$. Now (ii) implies that $c_0 = c_1$ and then from (i) it follows that $c_0 = c_1 = 1$. Finally, substituting all this into (iii), we get $2x_0^2 = \frac{2}{3}$ and hence that $x_0 = -1/\sqrt{3}$ and $x_1 = 1/\sqrt{3}$.

Hence we get the integration rule

$$\int_{-1}^{1} f(x)\, dx \approx f\!\left(\frac{-1}{\sqrt{3}}\right) + f\!\left(\frac{1}{\sqrt{3}}\right)$$

which has degree of precision 3 using just two integration points.

Taking $f(x) = \exp[-(x+1)^2/2]/\sqrt{2\pi}$ so that

$$I(f) = \frac{1}{\sqrt{2\pi}} \int_{-1}^{1} \exp\left(\frac{-(x+1)^2}{2}\right) dx$$

$$= \frac{1}{\sqrt{2\pi}} \int_{0}^{2} \exp\left(-\frac{x^2}{2}\right) dx \qquad (5.17)$$

we get

$$I(f) \approx \frac{\exp(1/\sqrt{3} - \tfrac{4}{3}) + \exp(-1/\sqrt{3} - \tfrac{2}{3})}{\sqrt{2\pi}} = 0.479\,84.$$

Comparing this with Example 5.2.3 we see that this result is more accurate than those obtained using the trapezium or Simpson's rule with five points.

(b) Here we seek three nodes x_0, x_1, x_2 and corresponding quadrature weights c_0, c_1, c_2. Following the same reasoning as above, we get the following equations.

   (i) For $f(x) = 1$, $I(f) = 2 = c_0 + c_1 + c_2$.
   (ii) For $f(x) = x$, $I(f) = 0 = c_0 x_0 + c_1 x_1 + c_2 x_2$.
   (iii) For $f(x) = x^2$, $I(f) = \tfrac{2}{3} = c_0 x_0^2 + c_1 x_1^2 + c_2 x_2^2$.
   (iv) For $f(x) = x^3$, $I(f) = 0 = c_0 x_0^3 + c_1 x_1^3 + c_2 x_2^3$.
   (v) For $f(x) = x^4$, $I(f) = \tfrac{2}{5} = c_0 x_0^4 + c_1 x_1^4 + c_2 x_2^4$.
   (vi) For $f(x) = x^5$, $I(f) = 0 = c_0 x_0^5 + c_1 x_1^5 + c_2 x_2^5$.

It is worthwhile to use a more sophisticated approach this time. The nodes x_0, x_1, x_2 are the roots of the cubic equation

$$p(x) = (x - x_0)(x - x_1)(x - x_2)$$

$$= 0.$$

We may write $p(x) = x^3 + \alpha x^2 + \beta x + \gamma$ for some, as yet unknown, coefficients α, β, γ. Now (iv) $+ \alpha$(iii) $+ \beta$(ii) $+ \gamma$(i) gives us

$$\frac{2\alpha}{3} + 2\gamma = c_0(x_0^3 + \alpha x_0^2 + \beta x_0 + \gamma) + c_1(x_1^3 + \alpha x_1^2 + \beta x_1 + \gamma)$$

$$+ c_2(x_2^3 + \alpha x_2^2 + \beta x_2 + \gamma)$$

$$= 0$$

since x_0, x_1, x_2 all satisfy $p(x) = 0$. Hence $\alpha = -3\gamma$.

Similarly, (v) $+ \alpha$(iv) $+ \beta$(iii) $+ \gamma$(ii) implies that $\beta = -\tfrac{3}{5}$ and (vi) $+ \alpha$(v) $+ \beta$(iv) $+ \gamma$(iii) implies that $\alpha = -5\gamma/3$. Thence we deduce $\alpha = \gamma = 0$ and so $p(x) = x^3 - 3x/5$. This has the roots $x_0 = -\sqrt{\tfrac{3}{5}}$, $x_1 = 0$ and $x_2 = \sqrt{\tfrac{3}{5}}$.

We can now use the original equations to find the weights which turn out to be $c_0 = c_2 = \frac{5}{9}$ and $c_1 = \frac{8}{9}$. Thus we have

$$\int_{-1}^{1} f(x)\, dx \approx \frac{(5f(-\sqrt{\tfrac{3}{5}}) + 8f(0) + 5f(\sqrt{\tfrac{3}{5}}))}{9} \tag{5.18}$$

which has degree of precision 5.

For the same example as above we get

$$I(f) \approx \frac{(5 \times 0.974\,92 + 8 \times 0.606\,53 + 5 \times 0.207\,09)}{9\sqrt{2\pi}}$$

$$= 0.477\,06$$

so that with just three points we have a result of greater precision than that given by the trapezium rule with nine or the midpoint rule with eight.

Unfortunately, this Gaussian quadrature approach does not lend itself readily to use within an automatic routine since the nodes and weights for one rule are not related in any simple way to those of any others. There has been considerable effort devoted to the development of efficient automatic integration routines based on Gaussian qaudrature rules but we do not pursue these here.

In Exercises 5.2, 7, you considered the ratio of the errors in S_2 and S_1 under the assumption that $f^{(4)}$ is approximately constant over the range of integration. We can repeat that calculation in slightly greater generality. Suppose that Simpson's rule is applied over the interval $[a, b]$ using N and then $2N$ equal subintervals and denote $(b-a)/4N$ by h. Then, by Theorem 5.2.1,

$$E(S_N) = \frac{-(b-a)(2h)^4 f^{(4)}(\theta_1)}{180}$$

and

$$E(S_{2N}) = \frac{-(b-a)h^4 f^{(4)}(\theta_2)}{180}$$

$$\approx \frac{E(S_N)}{16}$$

under the assumption that $f^{(4)}$ is roughly constant so that $f^{(4)}(\theta_1) \approx f^{(4)}(\theta_2)$. Now, $E(S_N) = I - S_N$ and $E(S_{2N}) = I - S_{2N}$ where I is the integral that we wish to find. Hence we can deduce that

$$I - S_N \approx 16(I - S_{2N})$$

and hence that

$$I \approx \frac{16S_{2N} - S_N}{15} \tag{5.19}$$

and this process should have eliminated the most significant contribution to the error.

The corresponding procedure with S_1 and S_2 yields

$$15I \approx 16[f(a) + 4f(a+h) + 2f(a+2h) + 4f(a+3h) + f(b)] \times \ldots$$

$$\times \frac{h}{3} - [f(a) + 4f(a+2h) + f(b)]\frac{2h}{3}$$

$$= [14f(a) + 64f(a+h) + 24f(a+2h) + 64f(a+3h) + 14f(b)]\frac{h}{3}$$

and therefore we have the five-point quadrature rule

$$I \approx \frac{2h}{45}[7f(a) + 32f(a+h) + 12f(a+2h) + 32f(a+3h) + f(b)]. \tag{5.20}$$

This formula is in fact the interpolatory quadrature rule using five equally spaced points and could therefore have been derived in the same way as the other interpolatory rules. The error in using this formula is of the form $Ch^6 f^{(6)}(\theta)$ and so we could repeat the above process of halving the step length and then eliminating the most significant part of the error to obtain a more accurate formula still. This is the basis of **Romberg integration**. In fact, we could have started the process from the trapezium rule in which case we would simply have rediscovered Simpson's rule which would then be given as

$$S_N = \frac{4T_{2N} - T_N}{3}. \tag{5.21}$$

To describe the process in more detail, it is convenient to introduce a systematic notation for the various estimates of the integral I. We denote by $R_{n,1}$ the value obtained by the trapezium rule using 2^{n-1} equal subintervals so that the process starts with

$$R_{1,1} = T_1$$

$$= \frac{(b-a)[f(a) + f(b)]}{2}.$$

Similarly, $R_{n,2}$ will denote the value obtained by Simpson's rule applied to 2^{n-1} equal subintervals. Then, using equation (5.21), we see that

$$R_{n,2} = \frac{4R_{n+1,1} - R_{n,1}}{3}.$$

Denoting the result of applying equation (5,20), again over 2^{n-1} equal subintervals, by $R_{n,3}$ we have

132

$$R_{n,3} = \frac{16R_{n+1,2} - R_{n,2}}{15}.$$

We can continue in this way as follows:

$R_{1,1}$

$R_{2,1}$ $R_{1,2}$

$R_{3,1}$ $R_{2,2}$ $R_{1,3}$

$R_{4,1}$ $R_{3,2}$ $R_{2,3}$ $R_{1,4}$

$R_{5,1}$ $R_{4,2}$ $R_{3,3}$ $R_{2,4}$ $R_{1,5}$

.   .   .   .   .   .

.   .   .   .

and it is fairly easy to see that the entries further to the right are obtained by an extension of the arguments used above. The general formula is

$$R_{n,k} = \frac{4^{k-1}R_{n+1,k-1} - R_{n,k-1}}{4^{k-1} - 1}. \tag{5.22}$$

We seek convergence of the entries down the top diagonal or the last row to the required accuracy, in which case we conclude that no further improvement is available since rules of different degrees of precision yield the same result.

Example 5.3.2

We shall again consider the integral

$$I(f) = \frac{1}{\sqrt{2\pi}} \int_0^2 \exp\left(-\frac{x^2}{2}\right) dx,$$

and use the results from Example 5.2.3. Thus

$R_{1,1} = T_1$

     $= 0.452\,93,$

$R_{2,1} = T_2$ $R_{1,2} = \dfrac{4R_{2,1} - R_{1,1}}{3}$

     $= 0.468\,44$ $= 0.473\,61$

                                 $= S_1,$

$R_{3,1} = 0.475\,01$ $R_{2,2} = 0.477\,20$ $R_{1,3} = \dfrac{16R_{2,2} - R_{1,2}}{15}$

                                                  $= 0.477\,44,$

$$R_{4,1} = 0.476\,69 \qquad R_{3,2} = 0.477\,25 \qquad R_{2,3} = 0.477\,25$$

$$R_{1,4} = \frac{64R_{2,3} - R_{1,3}}{63}$$
$$= 0.477\,25.$$

Here we see convergence of the two final entries in the current row. We conclude that the integral is 0.477 25 to five decimal places. The following program applies Romberg integration to this same problem with a more severe accuracy requirement.

PROGRAM 5.3.1

```
1    REM******APPROXIMATE EVALUATION OF INTEGRALS USING******
     REM******              ROMBERG INTEGRATION              ******
10 OPEN "RESULTS." FOR OUTPUT AS FILE £3
   PRINT £3, "EVALUATION OF INTEGRAL USING ROMBERG INTEGRATION"
   PRINT £3, "F(X) = EXP(−X↑2/2)"
   PRINT £3, "RANGE OF INTEGRATION IS [0,2]"
   PRINT £3, "TOLERANCE REQUIRED IS 1E − 6"
   DIMENSION M(10), R(2,10)
REM   THE ARRAY R(2,N) HOLDS THE CURRENT ROW OF THE ROMBERG ARRAY
REM   THE ARRAY R(1,N) HOLDS THE PREVIOUS ROW OF THE ARRAY

20 A = 0 \ B = 2 \ E = 1E − 6
   DEF FNF(X) = EXP(−X↑2/2)
   H = B − A \ P = 1
   R(2,1) = H*(FNF(A) + FNF(B))/2
REM   A,B ARE THE END-POINTS OF THE RANGE OF INTEGRATION

30 FOR N = 1 TO 9
     FOR I = 1 TO N \ R(1,I) = R(2,I) \ NEXT I
     H1 = H \ H = H/2
REM   H IS STEPLENGTH AND P IS THE NUMBER OF POINTS FOR MID-POINT RULE
31   Y = A \ M = 0
     FOR J = 1 TO P
        Y = Y + H \ M = M + FNF(Y)
     NEXT J
     M = M*H1
REM   M IS VALUE OF CURRENT MID-POINT RULE ESTIMATE
32   R(2,1) = (M + R(1,1))/2 \ C = 1
REM   C IS THE COEFFICIENT USED IN OBTAINING THE ARRAY
33   FOR K = 2 TO N + 1
        C = 4*C
        R(2,K) = (C*R(2,K − 1) − R(1,K − 1))/(C − 1)
     NEXT K
     IF ABS(R(2,N + 1) − R(2,N)) < E GOTO 40
   NEXT N
   PRINT £3, "FAILED TO ACHIEVE REQUIRED ACCURACY"
   GOTO 50

40 PRINT £3, "CONVERGED TO REQUIRED TOLERANCE"
50 PRINT £3, "LAST TWO ESTIMATES"; R(2,N), R(2,N + 1)
   STOP
   END
```

One thing to note in this program is that we have no need to store the full array but can *overwrite* the old array with the new one. In this particular case, two rows have been kept at each stage to make it easier to follow the flow of the program, but even this can and would be avoided in the most efficient implementation.

We finish this section with a brief introduction to the ideas of adaptive integration algorithms. These use the principle of subdividing the range of integration but without insisting on using uniform subdivision throughout the interval. To simplify the discussion, we restrict our attention to the adaptive use of Simpson's rule. There are two fundamentally different approaches available to us.

(a) Decide on an initial subdivision of the interval into N subintervals $[x_k, x_{k+1}]$ with $a = x_0 < x_1 < \ldots < x_N = b$. Use the composite Simpson's rule with continual halving in each of the subintervals in turn. (Typical choices of subdivision are to take five or 20 equal subintervals.)

(b) Start with the full interval. If the estimates of the integral for the current interval and the sum of the estimates for its two halves agree, then accept that partial result and move on to the next subinterval. If the estimates do not agree (to the required accuracy), then continue to work with just half the interval, leaving the other half to be dealt with later.

The details of such implementations can vary immensely. We illustrate these two approaches with a simple example.

Example 5.3.3

Evaluate

$$\pi = \int_0^1 \frac{4}{(1 + x^2)} \, dx \text{ to five decimal places.}$$

In order to obtain the required accuracy, we shall seek agreement to $2L \times 10^{-6}$ for any subinterval of length L. (For this particularly well-behaved function this is a very safe criterion.)

(a) Using five equal subdivisions and continual halving in each of these. Thus we seek agreement to 4×10^{-7} on each of the subintervals.

For $[0, 0.2]$, the sequence of composite Simpson's rule estimates is as follows:

using three points, $\qquad S_1 = 0.789\,591\,3$,

using five points, $S_2 = 0.789\,582\,8,$

using nine points, $S_4 = 0.789\,582\,3,$

using 17 points, $S_8 = 0.789\,582\,3.$

     For $[0.2, 0.4]$

$$S_1 = 0.732\,444\,3,$$

$$S_2 = 0.732\,443\,3,$$

$$S_4 = 0.732\,443\,3.$$

Similarly, for $[0.4, 0.6]$, $[0.6, 0.8]$ and $[0.8, 1.0]$, S_2 and S_4 agree sufficiently closely, giving estimates 0.639 652 4, 0.537 285 7 and 0.442 628 8 which then gives us the estimate

$$\pi \approx 3.141\,593\,0,$$

which is in fact accurate to six decimal places. This calculation used a total of 49 function evaluations provided that none is repeated.

(b) We begin with the whole interval $[0, 1]$. For any interval for which we do not have the required agreement between S_1 and S_2, we work on just the left-hand half until agreement is reached and then proceed to the next piece.

     Thus, we keep working with the left-hand half of the current interval until eventually we obtain agreement on $[0, 0.031\,25]$ where $S_2 = 0.124\,959\,334$. Next we move on to the other half of the interval $[0, 0.0625]$; that is, $[0.031\,25, 0.0625]$ where agreement is obtained immediately as it is on $[0.0625, 0.125]$. Eventually we obtain the estimate

$$\pi \approx 3.141\,592\,6,$$

having used the intervals $[x_k, x_{k+1}]$ where the end-points are 0, 0.031 25, 0.0625, 0.125, 0.1875, 0.25, 0.375, 0.5, 0.5625, 0.625, 0.6825, 0.75, 0.875 and 1. This used a total of 53 function evaluations.

EXERCISES 5.3

1 Find the Gaussian quadrature rule using four points on the interval $[-1, 1]$. What is its degree of precision? Use this formula to estimate the integral of $\sqrt{1 + x}$ over this interval.

2 Modify Program 5.3.1 to estimate the integral of Exercises 5.3, **1**, to six decimal places.

3 Write an adaptive integration program using N equal subintervals and

the composite Simpson's rule with continual halving in each. (Embed a modified version of Program 5.2.1 in an appropriate loop.) Test this by evaluating the integral of Exercises 5.3, **1**, to six decimal places.

5.4 NUMERICAL DIFFERENTIATION

In some respects the methods of numerical differentiation are similar to those of numerical integration in that they are based on differentiating an interpolation polynomial. However, there is one major and important difference. We saw in the previous sections that numerical integration is numerically a highly satisfactory operation with results of high accuracy often being obtainable in an economic way. This is a consequence of the fact that integration tends to smooth out the errors in the polynomial approximations being used. Unfortunately, as we can see from Fig. 5.2, this is certainly not the case for differentiation which will often exaggerate the error in the original approximation.

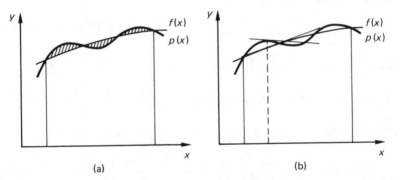

Fig. 5.2 (a) Integration: the difference in the areas under the two curves cancel. (b) Differentiation: the difference in the slopes is significant

For this reason, numerical differentiation is best avoided whenever possible. We have already seen in discussing Newton's method and the secant method (section 2.4) for solving an equation that, if the actual *value* of the derivative is of secondary importance, then a simple divided-difference approximation to this derivative can be satisfactory. We begin our very brief look at this topic with this approximation.

By definition

$$f'(x_0) = \lim_{h \to 0}\left(\frac{f(x_0 + h) - f(x_0)}{h}\right)$$

from which we get the simple approximation

137

$$f'(x_0) \approx \frac{f(x_0 + h) - f(x_0)}{h}$$

$$= f[x_0, x_0 + h] \qquad (5.23)$$

for some small h. (This is precisely the approximation used for the secant method.) Now, by the mean-value theorem,

$$f[x_0, x_0 + h] = f'(\theta_1)$$

for some point θ_1 between x_0 and $x_0 + h$ and hence the error in equation (5.23) is given by

$$f'(x_0) - f'(\theta_1) = (x_0 - \theta_1) f''(\theta_2),$$

where θ_2 lies between x_0 and θ_1. Using Taylor's theorem it can be shown quite easily that this error can be written for some θ between x_0 and $x_0 + h$ as

$$f'(x_0) - f[x_0, x_0 + h] = \frac{-hf''(\theta)}{2}. \qquad (5.24)$$

We can use the corresponding expansions for $f(x_0 - h)$ and $f(x_0 + h)$ to obtain improved estimates. Now

$$f(x_0 + h) = f(x_0) + hf'(x_0) + \frac{h^2 f''(x_0)}{2} + \frac{h^3 f^{(3)}(\theta_+)}{6}$$

and

$$f(x_0 - h) = f(x_0) - hf'(x_0) + \frac{h^2 f''(x_0)}{2} - \frac{h^3 f^{(3)}(\theta_-)}{6}.$$

Subtracting the second of these from the first and rearranging yields

$$f'(x_0) - \frac{f(x_0 + h) - f(x_0 - h)}{2h} = \frac{h^2 [f^{(3)}(\theta_+) + f^{(3)}(\theta_-)]}{12}; \qquad (5.25)$$

then, applying the intermediate value theorem to $f^{(3)}$ (assuming that this is continuous), we see that the error can be written in the form $h^2 f^{(3)}(\theta)/6$ for some $\theta \in (x_0 - h, x_0 + h)$. Figure 5.3 shows why we should expect the symmetric approximation in equation (5.25) to be better than that given by equation (5.23).

The fact that the approximation $[f(x_0 + h) - f(x_0 - h)]/2h$ in equation (5.25) can also be derived by differentiating the interpolation polynomial agreeing with f at the three points $x_0 - h$, x_0 and $x_0 + h$ is left as an exercise. Using either of these approaches, we can also obtain the fourth-order approximation

$$f'(x_0) \approx \frac{2f(x_0 - 2h) - 16f(x_0 - h) + 16f(x_0 + h) - 2f(x_0 + 2h)}{24h}.$$

$$(5.26)$$

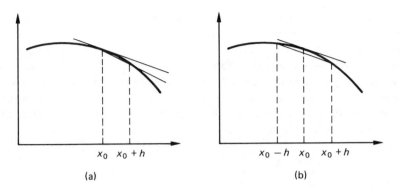

Fig. 5.3 (a) Equation (5.23): tangent and chord have quite distinct slopes. (b) Equation (5.25): tangent and chord have very similar slopes

---

Example 5.4.1

Estimate $f'(0.7)$ with $f(x) = \ln x$ using equations (5.23), (5.25) and (5.26) with $h = 0.1$ and then $h = 0.01$.

Using equation (5.23) we have, for $h = 0.1$, $f'(0.7) \approx 10[\ln(0.8) - \ln(0.7)]$ $= 1.3353$ or, alternatively, $f'(0.7) \approx 10[\ln(0.7) - \ln(0.6)] = 1.5415$.

The corresponding values using $h = 0.01$ are 1.41846 and 1.43887 which are certainly much closer to the true value of 1.42857.

Using equation (5.25) with $h = 0.1$, $f'(0.7) \approx 5[\ln(0.8) - \ln(0.6)] = 1.4384$ and, with $h = 0.01$, $f'(0.7) \approx 50[\ln(0.71) - \ln(0.69)] = 1.42867$.

Equation (5.26) gives the estimates 1.42806 and, with $h = 0.01$, 1.4285714 which is accurate to all the figures shown.

We see clearly from the above example that, in order to obtain even reasonable accuracy for a very well-behaved function, it is necessary to use a small step length and to avoid formulae of very low degree of precision. It is the need for small step lengths, in particular, which results in the loss of numerical stability because, as h approaches zero, the effect of rounding error in the data begins to dominate the truncation error of the process. To see this, consider the overall error in equation (5.23) assuming that the function values $f(x_0)$ and $f(x_0 + h)$ are known to have rounding errors bounded by δ, say. Denote the true values by f_0 and f_1, respectively, and the computed or given values by $\hat{f}_0$ and $\hat{f}_1$. Then

$$\left| f'(x_0) - \frac{(\hat{f}_1 - \hat{f}_0)}{h} \right| \leqslant \left| f'(x_0) - \frac{(f_1 - f_0)}{h} \right| + \left| \frac{(f_1 - f_0)}{h} - \frac{(\hat{f}_1 - \hat{f}_0)}{h} \right|$$

and, by equation (5.24), the first term is of the form Ch while the second is

139

bounded by $2\delta/h$. As h becomes small, this second term can grow without bound. Clearly, if the data are subject to experimental error, the use of numerical differentiation is unreliable.

In the case of numerical differentiation, we must also consider the problem of approximating higher derivatives. The same basic approaches of differentiation of an interpolation polynomial or use of Taylor's theorem can be used again. For example, adding third-order Taylor expansions for $f(x_0 \pm h)$, we obtain the approximation

$$f''(x_0) \approx \frac{f(x_0 + h) - 2f(x_0) + f(x_0 - h)}{h^2}, \qquad (5.27)$$

which has the error $h^2 f^{(4)}(0)/12$. Similarly, we can obtain the five-point formula

$$f''(x_0) \approx \frac{-f(x_0 + 2h) + 16f(x_0 + h) - 30f(x_0) + 16f(x_0 - h) - f(x_0 - 2h)}{12h^2},$$

$$(5.28)$$

which has a truncation error of order h^4.

Example 5.4.2

Again, taking $f(x) = \ln x$ and $x_0 = 0.7$, we get, using equation (5.27),

with $h = 0.1$ $\quad f''(0.7) \approx 100[\ln(0.8) - 2\ln(0.7) + \ln(0.6)]$

$$\approx -2.0619,$$

with $h = 0.01$ $\quad f''(0.7) \approx -2.0410.$

Using equation (5.28) gives

with $h = 0.1$ $\quad f''(0.7) \approx -2.039\,59,$

with $h = 0.01$ $\quad f''(0.7) \approx -2.040\,816\,3,$

which is in error by 5 in the last place.

It should be noted here that, with higher-order derivatives, the potential for rounding errors in the data to overwhelm the truncation error of the approximation is increased and such formulae are therefore even less reliable.

EXERCISES 5.4

1 Derive equation (5.25) by differentiating the interpolation polynomial which agrees with f at the points $x_0 - h$, x_0 and $x_0 + h$.

2 Derive the equations (5.27) and (5.28) either from Taylor series expansions or by differentiating the appropriate interpolation polynomials.

3 Find the five-point formula for estimating $f^{(3)}(x_0)$. Test it with $x = 0.5$ and $f(x) = \ln x$.

4 Use the approximations (5.23), (5.25) and (5.26) with $h = 1, 0.1, 0.01$ and 0.001 to estimate $f'(x_0)$ for $f(x) = \exp x$ and $x_0 = 2$. Repeat this for the second-derivative approximations (5.27) and (5.28).

5.5 MAXIMA AND MINIMA

In this section, we introduce some of the numerical techniques for finding turning points of a function f. Such points satisfy the condition $f'(x) = 0$ and so the techniques of chapter 2 can be used to find solutions of this equation. However, this is not always a very sensible approach to the problem since there is then no guarantee that we do in fact find a turning point rather than a stationary point of inflexion. It is also the case that such methods cannot distinguish between maximum and minimum values of the function.

We shall concentrate on the problem of finding a **local minimum** of f. If a local maximum is required, we can simply apply our methods to the minimisation of $-f(x)$. Thus, we seek a point x^* which satisfies the condition

$$f(x^*) \leqslant f(x) \qquad \text{for all } x \text{ sufficiently close to } x^*. \qquad (5.29)$$

Most numerical methods for the minimisation of a function of a single variable work on the principle of reducing an interval in which the minimum is known to lie and on which the function is assumed to be **unimodal**—that is, it has only one turning point within this **bracket**, as it is called. The choice of a specific technique depends on what information is available to us; in particular the availability or otherwise of the derivative of f is of fundamental importance—and this applies even to the finding of a suitable bracket for x^*.

To obtain a bracket without using the derivative, we require three points $x < y < z$ such that $f(x) > f(y)$ and $f(z) > f(y)$ whereas, if the derivative is available, we simply seek two points $x < y$ for which $f'(x) < 0 < f'(y)$. In general, we start with an initial guess x_0 and a step length h (positive or negative) and generate new points x_k, $k = 1, 2, \ldots$, according to the relation

$$x_k = x_{k-1} + 2^{k-1}h \qquad (5.30)$$

until one of these conditions is satisfied. In equation (5.30), it is apparent that the step taken from x_{k-1} to x_k is doubled each time so that, if x_0 is well removed from x^*, we do not require a large number of small steps. Generally speaking, the methods which are used to refine the bracket once it is obtained are so much more efficient that this will still result in an overall saving of computational effort.

We make no effort here to describe a foolproof algorithm for the bracketing procedure as this requires a considerable amount of (not very instructive) detail to cover all the different special cases which can arise. The general approach is illustrated in the following.

Example 5.5.1

Bracket the minimum of

$$f(x) = x + \frac{1}{x^2}$$

both with and without derivatives starting with $x_0 = 1$ and $h = 0.1$.
  Firstly, without derivatives, we have

$$x_0 = 1 \qquad\qquad f(x_0) = 2.0000,$$
$$x_1 = x_0 + h = 1.1 \qquad\qquad f(x_1) = 1.9264,$$
$$x_2 = x_1 + 2h = 1.3 \qquad\qquad f(x_2) = 1.8917,$$
$$x_3 = x_2 + 4h = 1.7 \qquad\qquad f(x_3) = 2.0460,$$

and, since $f(x_2) < f(x_1), f(x_3)$, it follows that there is a local minimum in $[1.1, 1.7]$.
  Using the derivative which in this case is $f'(x) = 1 - 2/x^3$, we have

$$x_0 = 1 \qquad\qquad f'(x_0) = -1.0000,$$
$$x_1 = 1.1 \qquad\qquad f'(x_1) = -0.5026,$$
$$x_2 = 1.3 \qquad\qquad f'(x_2) = 0.0897,$$

and so we obtain the bracket $[1.1, 1.3]$.

If the derivative is available, then it is usually advantageous to use it. Since only two points are necessary to identify a bracket and the step length doubles with each step, the bracket obtained with derivatives (using the same x_0 and h) will be at most two-thirds of the length of that obtained otherwise.
  Once a bracket has been obtained, there are many different ways of reducing this to get accurate estimates of the true minimum point x^*. In this section, we consider just two methods which are both based on finding the local minimum of an interpolation polynomial. The quadratic search does not use derivatives while the cubic search does.
  For the quadratic search, as the name suggests, the position of x^* is estimated by minimising a quadratic interpolation polynomial which agrees with f at three points. The points are then adjusted and the process repeated

until the required accuracy is achieved. The process is greatly simplified if the points used at each stage are equally spaced.

Suppose then that we already have a bracket $[x_0, x_2]$ for the minimum of f and let x_1 be the midpoint of this interval. Thus

$$x_2 = x_1 + h = x_0 + 2h,$$

where now $h = (x_2 - x_0)/2$, and we suppose that $f_1 < f_0, f_2$ where $f_i = f(x_i)$ for $i = 0, 1, 2$. Now the quadratic agreeing with f at these points can be written using the divided-difference formula as

$$p(x) = f_1 + (x - x_1)f[x_0, x_1] + (x - x_1)(x - x_0)f[x_0, x_1, x_2]$$

$$= f_1 + \frac{(x - x_0 - h)(f_1 - f_0)}{h} + \frac{(x - x_0 - h)(x - x_0)(f_2 - 2f_1 + f_0)}{2h^2}$$

and, differentiating this, we find that p has its minimum at

$$x' = x_1 + \frac{f_0 - f_2}{f_0 - 2f_1 + f_2} \frac{h}{2} \tag{5.31}$$

which lies in $[x_1 - h/2, x_1 + h/2]$.

Now, if $f(x') < f_1$, we can use x' as the midpoint of a new interval half the length of the previous one. Otherwise we retain x_1 as the midpoint but still halve the interval length. It only remains to check that the new x_0, x_1, x_2 provide a bracket for the true minimum and that the process can be repeated until the length of the bracketing interval is within the specified tolerance.

The convergence of this process is established in Theorem 5.5.1 below but first we have an example.

Example 5.5.2

Use a quadratic search to minimise the function $x + 1/x^2$.

We known from Example 5.5.1 that $x^* \in [1.1, 1.7]$. (The shorter bracket relied on the use of derivatives which we are assuming here are unavailable.) Thus we have initially $x_0 = 1.1$, $x_1 = 1.4$ and $x_2 = 1.7$ with respective function values 1.9264, 1.9102 and 2.0460 and $h = 0.3$. Hence

$$x' = 1.4 + \frac{(1.9264 - 2.0460) \times 0.3}{(1.9264 - 2 \times 1.9102 + 2.0460) \times 2}$$

$$= 1.2820$$

and

$$f(x') = 1.8904 < f_1.$$

The new h is 0.15 and with $x_1 = 1.282$ we have $x_0 = 1.132$ and $x_2 = 1.432$. The corresponding function values are then 1.9124, 1.8904 and 1.9197 from which we get

$$x' = 1.2713$$

and

$$f(x') = 1.8900.$$

For the third iteration, therefore, $x_1 = 1.2713$ and $h = 0.075$, $x_0 = 1.1963$, $x_2 = 1.3463$ with $f_0 = 1.8950$, $f_2 = 1.8980$. This yields $x' = 1.2626$ and $f(x') = 1.8899$.

At this stage, we thus have $x^* \approx 1.2626$ with error less than $h/2 = 0.0375$.

THEOREM 5.5.1   Let f be a unimodal function whose minimum x^* is known to lie in the interval $[a, b]$. Then the sequence of points x_1 generated by the quadratic search algorithm converges to x^*.

Proof   Denote by $x_0^{(n)}, x_1^{(n)}, x_2^{(n)}$ the sequences of points x_0, x_1 and x_2 generated by this method. We begin with $x_0^{(0)} = a$ and $x_2^{(0)} = b$ and at each iteration of the algorithm the length of the interval is halved so that

$$x_2^{(n)} - x_0^{(n)} = \frac{x_2^{(n-1)} - x_0^{(n-1)}}{2}$$

$$= \frac{x_2^{(0)} - x_0^{(0)}}{2^n},$$

from which it follows that $x_2^{(n)} - x_0^{(n)} \to 0$ as $n \to \infty$. Moreover, at each stage, we ensure that $x_0^{(n)} < x^* < x_2^{(n)}$ and so it must follow that $x_2^{(n)} - x^* \to 0$ and $x_0^{(n)} - x^* \to 0$ as $n \to \infty$. Since $x_0^{(n)} < x_1^{(n)} < x_2^{(n)}$, the result follows by the sandwich rule.

The following program implements the quadratic search within a bracket which must be supplied by the user.

PROGRAM 5.5.1

```
10 OPEN "MINIMUM.LIS" FOR OUTPUT AS FILE £3
   REM ****** MINIMIZATION OF A FUNCTION BY QUADRATIC SEARCH ******
20 E = 1E − 2
   DEF FNF(X) = X + 1/X/X
   REM   E IS THE FINAL TOLERANCE
30 PRINT "TYPE IN THE END-POINTS OF THE INITIAL BRACKET"
   INPUT A, B
   C = (A + B)/2 \ H = C − A
   FA = FNF(A) \ FB = FNF(B) \ FC = FNF(C)
   EVAL = 3
```

```
40 IF FC < FA AND FC < FB THEN 70
50 IF FA ⩽ FC THEN B = C \ C = A \ FB = FC \ FC = FA
                A = C − H \ FA = FNF(A)
            ELSE A = C \ C = B \ FA = FC \ FC = FB
                B = C + H \ FB = FNF(B)
   REM   THIS HAS SHIFTED THE BRACKET LEFT OR RIGHT IF NECESSARY
   REM      TO ENSURE THAT A BRACKET IS MAINTAINED
60 EVAL = EVAL + I \ GOTO 40

70 PRINT £3, A, C, B
   PRINT £3, FA, FC, FB
   PRINT £3,
   IF H < E THEN 100

80 H = H/2 \ C1 = C + (FA − FB)*H/(FB − 2*FC + FA) \ F1 = FNF(C1) \ EVAL = EVAL + 1
   IF F1 < FC THEN C = C1 \ FC = F1
90 A = C − H \ B = C + H \ FA = FNF(A) \ FB = FNF(B) \ EVAL = EVAL + 2
   GOTO 40

100 PRINT £3, "FINAL BRACKET IS"; A, B
    PRINT £3, "BEST POINT FOUND IS"; C; "WITH FUNCTION VALUE"; FC
    PRINT £3, "TOTAL NUMBER OF FUNCTION EVALUATIONS USED IS"; EVAL
120 STOP
    END
```

With the initial bracket $[1.15, 1.63]$ (which would be obtained by the same procedure as before using $h = 0.01$), we get the output

0.91	1.15	1.39
2.11758	1.90614	1.90757
1.14839	1.26839	1.38839
1.90666	1.88997	1.90716
1.20749	1.26749	1.32749
1.89335	1.88995	1.89495
1.23175	1.26175	1.29175
1.89086	1.88989	1.89105
1.24539	1.26039	1.27539
1.89014	1.88988	1.89016
1.25254	1.26004	1.26754
1.88995	1.88988	1.88995

FINAL BRACKET IS 1.25254   1.26754
BEST POINT FOUND IS 1.26004 WITH FUNCTION VALUE 1.88988
TOTAL NUMBER OF FUNCTION EVALUATIONS USED IS 19

Note here that for the first iteration the bracket used is not the one given above. Although $[1.15, 1.63]$ is a bracket for x^*, the midpoint does not yield a smaller function value than those at both end-points and so the initial bracket is shifted to the left as a result of the tests in lines 40 and 50.

We now turn to the cubic search method which uses values of both the function f and its derivative f' at two points. Suppose then that we have

$x_0 < x_1$ such that $f'(x_0) < 0 < f'(x_1)$ and let p be the cubic which agrees with f and f' at x_0 and x_1. Write

$$p(x) = ax^3 + bx^2 + cx + d.$$

Then p has its turning points at $[-b \pm (b^2 - 3ac)^{-1/2}]/3a$ and one of these—the local minimum—must lie in (x_0, x_1) since $p'(x_0) < 0 < p'(x_1)$.

Now, if $a < 0$, then the local minimum of p is at the smaller of these values which corresponds to taking the $+$ sign in the above expression whereas, if $a > 0$, the minimum is the right-hand turning point which again corresponds to the $+$ sign. Thus, in both cases, we set

$$x^+ = \frac{-b + (b^2 - 3ac)^{1/2}}{3a}. \tag{5.32}$$

If now $f'(x^+) < 0$, then we can replace x_0 by x^+; otherwise we can replace x_1 by x^+ and so obtain a smaller bracket for the true minimum x^*.

The only remaining difficulty is to obtain expressions for the coefficients of p. These are the solutions of the system of equations

$$\begin{pmatrix} x_0^3 & x_0^2 & x_0 & 1 \\ x_1^3 & x_1^2 & x_1 & 1 \\ 3x_0^2 & 2x_0 & 1 & 0 \\ 3x_1^2 & 2x_1 & 1 & 0 \end{pmatrix} \begin{pmatrix} a \\ b \\ c \\ d \end{pmatrix} = \begin{pmatrix} f_0 \\ f_1 \\ f'_0 \\ f'_1 \end{pmatrix}.$$

The value of d does not affect the position of the minimum and so need not be found; the others are given by

$$a = X(G - 2H),$$

$$b = H - (x_1 + 2x_0)a,$$

and

$$c = F - (x_0^2 + x_0 x_1 + x_1^2)a - (x_0 + x_1)b$$

where

$$X = \frac{1}{x_1 - x_0},$$

$$F = X(f_1 - f_0),$$

$$G = X(f'_1 - f'_0)$$

and

$$H = X(F - f'_0).$$

Example 5.5.3

Minimise $x + 1/x^2$ by the cubic search.

We have the bracket $[1.1, 1.3]$ from Example 5.5.1 and so take $x_0 = 1.1$ and $x_1 = 1.3$. Then

$$f_0 = 1.9264,$$
$$f_1 = 1.8917,$$
$$f'_0 = -0.5026,$$
$$f'_1 = 0.0897,$$

from which we obtain

$$X = \frac{1}{1.3 - 1.1}$$
$$= 5,$$
$$F = 5(1.8917 - 1.9264)$$
$$= -0.1735,$$
$$G = 5(0.0897 + 0.5026) = 2.9615,$$
$$H = 5(-0.1735 + 0.5026)$$
$$= 1.6455.$$

Hence $a = -1.6475$, $b = 7.4118$ and $c = -10.8281$ and then from equation (5.32) we deduce that $x^+ = 1.2588$ and then $f'(x^+) = -0.0027 < 0$.

For the next iteration, we replace x_0 by this x^+ and so have

$x_0 = 1.2588$	$f_0 = 1.8899$	$f'_0 = -0.0027,$
$x_1 = 1.3$	$f_1 = 1.8917$	$f'_1 = 0.0897,$

from which we obtain the next $x^+ = 1.2600$ and $f'(x^+) = 0.0002$ and so, after just two iterations, we have the bracket $[1.2588, 1.2600]$ for the minimum of f which is of course at $x^* = 2^{1/3} = 1.25992$ to five decimal places.

This rapid convergence to the minimum is entirely typical of this method which forms the basis of most of the so-called line-search techniques used within efficient routines for the minimisation of a differentiable function of several variables—a subject which is beyond the scope of the present work.

EXERCISES 5.5

1 Find a bracket for the minimum of $[(x+1)^2 + 1](x-2)^2$ starting from 0.1 with step length 0.1 both with and without derivatives.

2 Use the quadratic search method on the bracket (without derivatives) from Exercises 5.5, **1**, to find the minimum with an error less than 0.1.

3 Derive the equations for the coefficients of the cubic search polynomial for the special case where $x_0 = 0$.

4 Apply the cubic search technique to the bracket (with derivatives) obtained in Exercises 5.5, **1**. Stop when $f'(x^+) < 1\text{E}{-}2$.

6 DIFFERENTIAL EQUATIONS

6.1 INTRODUCTION

In this chapter, we introduce some of the basic approaches to the numerical solution of differential equations concentrating largely on the first-order **initial-value** problem which takes the form

$$y' = f(x, y) \qquad y(x_0) = y_0. \tag{6.1}$$

Most of the methods which we consider are based on the use of a Taylor series to approximate the value

$$y(x_1) = y(x_0 + h_0). \tag{6.2}$$

The resulting approximation is denoted by y_1. The idea can be reapplied to obtain y_2, an approximation to $y(x_2) = y(x_1 + h_1)$, where h_1 may or may not be the same as h_0, and so on throughout the range of x. (Note that the notation here is different from our earlier use of, say, f_k for the *exact* value of $f(x_k)$.)

We thus set

$$y_1 = y_0 + h_0 y_0' + \frac{h_0^2 y_0''}{2} + \ldots + \frac{h_0^N y_0^{(N)}}{N!}, \tag{6.3}$$

where the various derivative values can be obtained by differentiating the differential equation just as we did in the series solution of such an equation in section 3.6.

In many of the simpler methods the step length h is held fixed throughout the computation. With $N = 1$ in equation (6.3) this gives rise to **Euler's method** in which we have

$$y_1 = y_0 + h y_0'$$

$$= y_0 + h f(x_0, y_0)$$

or, in general,

$$y_{k+1} = y_k + hf(x_k, y_k). \qquad (6.4)$$

Note here that we would ideally like to set

$$y_{k+1} = y(x_k) + hf(x_k, y(x_k)),$$

but of course these true values are not available after the first step. This use of approximate values in generating subsequent approximations can lead to a serious build-up of the error, as we can see from Fig. 6.1. To see what is happening here, recall that our differential equation (6.1) will generally have a unique solution satisfying any given initial condition. Thus there is a *different* solution for the initial-value problem

$$y' = f(x, y) \qquad y(x_1) = y_1,$$

and the estimated value y_2 is obtained by approximating this latter, and *unwanted*, solution at x_2.

To illustrate the behaviour of the various methods which we discuss in this chapter, we shall consider the numerical solution of the differential equation

$$y' = 3x^2 y \qquad y(0) = 1, \qquad (6.5)$$

which has the analytic solution $y = \exp(x^3)$.

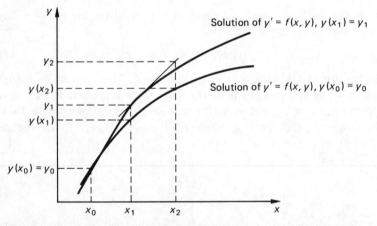

Fig. 6.1 Accumulation of error for Euler's method

Example 6.1.1

Solve the differential equation (6.5) in $[0, 1]$ using Euler's method with $h = 0.1$.

The values obtained by Euler's method and the exact values are

$$y_1 = y_0 + hf(x_0, y_0) \qquad\qquad y(0.1) = 1.001\,000\,5,$$
$$= 1.000\,000\,0 + 0.1 \times 3 \times 0^2 \times 1$$
$$= 1.000\,000\,0$$
$$y_2 = 1.000\,000\,0 + 0.3 \times 0.1^2 \times 1.000\,000\,0 \qquad y(0.2) = 1.008\,032\,1,$$
$$= 1.003\,000\,0$$
$$y_3 = 1.003\,000\,0 + 0.3 \times 0.2^2 \times 1.003\,000\,0 \qquad y(0.3) = 1.027\,367\,8,$$
$$= 1.015\,036\,0$$
$$y_4 = 1.015\,036\,0 + 0.3 \times 0.3^2 \times 1.015\,036\,0 \qquad y(0.4) = 1.066\,092\,4,$$
$$= 1.042\,442\,0$$
$$y_5 = 1.042\,442\,0 + 0.3 \times 0.4^2 \times 1.042\,442\,0 \qquad y(0.5) = 1.133\,148\,5,$$
$$= 1.092\,479\,2$$
$$y_6 = 1.174\,415\,1 \qquad\qquad\qquad\qquad\quad y(0.6) = 1.241\,102\,4,$$
$$y_7 = 1.301\,252\,0 \qquad\qquad\qquad\qquad\quad y(0.7) = 1.409\,168\,8,$$
$$y_8 = 1.492\,536\,0 \qquad\qquad\qquad\qquad\quad y(0.8) = 1.668\,625\,1,$$
$$y_9 = 1.779\,102\,9 \qquad\qquad\qquad\qquad\quad y(0.9) = 2.073\,006\,6,$$
$$y_{10} = 2.211\,424\,9 \qquad\qquad\qquad\qquad\quad y(1.0) = 2.718\,281\,8.$$

We see that the approximate solution is falling further and further behind the true solution. This is caused, in this case, by the fact that the derivative of the solution is a rapidly increasing function.

Clearly, Euler's method is not itself going to be sufficient to generate accurate solutions but it does provide the basis of some of the more successful approaches to the problem which use values of the function at more than one point in order to get higher-order agreement with the Taylor series in the computation of the next one. We consider these ideas in the next two sections.

6.2 RUNGE–KUTTA METHODS

The basic idea of the **Runge–Kutta methods** is to insert extra points between x_k and x_{k+1} which are effectively used to provide approximations to some of the higher derivatives in the Taylor series and so to improve the resulting approximation to $y(x_{k+1})$. The general derivation of these methods is somewhat complicated and we shall content ourselves here with an indication of where the methods come from and some examples.

To illustrate the ideas, consider equation (6.3) with $N = 2$ and fixed step length h, that is,

$$y_1 = y_0 + hy_0' + \frac{h^2 y_0''}{2},$$

or, in general,

$$y_{k+1} = y_k + hy_k' + \frac{h^2 y_k''}{2} = y_k + hf(x_k, y_k) + \frac{h^2 y_k''}{2}. \tag{6.6}$$

Now applying the simplest of our numerical differentiation formulae (5.23) to y' we have, for some step length h^*,

$$y_k'' \approx \frac{y'(x_k + h^*) - y'(x_k)}{h^*}$$

$$= \frac{f(x_k + h^*, y(x_k + h^*)) - f(x_k, y(x_k))}{h^*}$$

and, with $y(x_k) \approx y_k$ and $y(x_k + h^*) \approx y_k + h^* f(x_k, y_k)$, this yields

$$y_k'' \approx \frac{f(x_k + h^*, y_k + h^* f(x_k, y_k)) - f(x_k, y_k)}{h^*}. \tag{6.7}$$

Now, writing $h^* = ah$ and substituting equation (6.7) into equation (6.6), we get

$$y_{k+1} = y_k + hy_k' + \frac{h^2 [f(x_k + ah, y_k + ahf(x_k, y_k)) - f(x_k, y_k)]}{2ah}$$

$$= y_k + h\left(1 - \frac{1}{2a}\right) f(x_k, y_k) + \frac{hf(x_k + ah, y_k + ahf(x_k, y_k))}{2a},$$

which, in turn, can be written

$$y_{k+1} = y_k + c_1 k_1 + c_2 k_2, \tag{6.8}$$

where $c_1 = h(1 - 1/2a)$, $c_2 = h/2a$, $k_1 = f(x_k, y_k)$ and $k_2 = f(x_k + ah, y_k + ahk_1)$.

For such a *two-stage* formula, there is therefore one degree of freedom—the choice of a. With $a = \frac{1}{2}$, we get the **corrected Euler method**:

$$y_{k+1} = y_k + hk_2 \tag{6.9}$$

where $k_1 = f(x_k, y_k)$ and $k_2 = f(x_k + h/2, y_k + hk_1/2)$. With $a = \frac{2}{3}$, we have **Heun's method**:

$$y_{k+1} = y_k + \frac{h(k_1 + 3k_2)}{4} \tag{6.10}$$

where $k_1 = f(x_k, y_k)$ and $k_2 = f(x_k + 2h/3, y_k + 2hk_1/3)$.

Example 6.2.1

To our standard example (Example 6.1.1), we apply the following two formulae:

(a) equation (6.9) (the corrected Euler method);
(b) equation (6.10) (Heun's method).

(a) The corrected Euler method gives

$k = 0$:	$k_1 = 0.000\,000\,0$	$k_2 = 0.007\,500\,0$	and so y_1	$= 1.000\,750\,0$,
$k = 1$:	$k_1 = 0.030\,022\,5$	$k_2 = 0.067\,651\,9$	and so y_2	$= 1.007\,515\,2$,
$k = 2$:	$k_1 = 0.120\,901\,8$	$k_2 = 0.190\,042\,5$	and so y_3	$= 1.026\,519\,5$,
$k = 3$:	$k_1 = 0.277\,160\,2$	$k_2 = 0.382\,338\,7$	and so y_4	$= 1.064\,753\,3$,
$k = 4$:	$k_1 = 0.511\,081\,5$	$k_2 = 0.662\,361\,7$	and so y_5	$= 1.130\,989\,5$,
$k = 5$:	$k_1 = 0.848\,242\,1$	$k_2 = 1.064\,862\,0$	and so y_6	$= 1.237\,475\,7$,
$k = 6$:	$k_1 = 1.336\,473\,7$	$k_2 = 1.653\,199\,5$	and so y_7	$= 1.402\,795\,6$,
$k = 7$:	$k_1 = 2.062\,109\,6$	$k_2 = 2.541\,208\,1$	and so y_8	$= 1.656\,916\,5$,
$k = 8$:	$k_1 = 3.181\,279\,6$	$k_2 = 3.936\,137\,6$	and so y_9	$= 2.050\,530\,2$,
$k = 9$:	$k_1 = 4.982\,788\,4$	$k_2 = 6.226\,355\,5$	and so y_{10}	$= 2.673\,165\,8$.

We see that these results provide much better approximations to the true solution with the overall error in $y(1.0)$ being reduced to about 0.04—an improvement by a factor of about 12 compared with Euler's method in Example 6.1.1.

(b) Heun's method gives

$k = 0$:	$k_1 = 0.000\,000\,0$	$k_2 = 0.013\,333\,3$	and so y_1	$= 1.001\,000\,0$,
$k = 1$:	$k_1 = 0.030\,030\,0$	$k_2 = 0.083\,583\,5$	and so y_2	$= 1.008\,019\,5$,
$k = 2$:	$k_1 = 0.120\,962\,3$	$k_2 = 0.216\,764\,5$	and so y_3	$= 1.027\,300\,9$,
$k = 3$:	$k_1 = 0.277\,371\,2$	$k_2 = 0.421\,802\,9$	and so y_4	$= 1.065\,870\,4$,
$k = 4$:	$k_1 = 0.511\,617\,7$	$k_2 = 0.718\,652\,4$	and so y_5	$= 1.132\,559\,8$,
$k = 5$:	$k_1 = 0.849\,419\,8$	$k_2 = 1.145\,584\,2$	and so y_6	$= 1.239\,714\,1$,
$k = 6$:	$k_1 = 1.338\,891\,2$	$k_2 = 1.771\,964\,7$	and so y_7	$= 1.406\,083\,7$,
$k = 7$:	$k_1 = 2.066\,943\,1$	$k_2 = 2.722\,374\,9$	and so y_8	$= 1.661\,935\,4$,
$k = 8$:	$k_1 = 3.190\,916\,0$	$k_2 = 4.224\,241\,0$	and so y_9	$= 2.058\,526\,4$,
$k = 9$:	$k_1 = 5.002\,219\,1$	$k_2 = 6.705\,594\,8$	and so y_{10}	$= 2.686\,501\,5$.

which we see represents a further improvement of about 20% in the accumulated error in $y(1.0)$.

One of the most widely used of the Runge–Kutta formulae is the classical four-stage formula:

$$y_{k+1} = y_k + \frac{h(k_1 + 2k_2 + 2k_3 + k_4)}{6}, \qquad (6.11)$$

where

$$k_1 = f(x_k, y_k),$$

$$k_2 = f\left(x_k + \frac{h}{2}, y_k + \frac{hk_1}{2}\right),$$

$$k_3 = f\left(x_k + \frac{h}{2}, y_k + \frac{hk_2}{2}\right),$$

$$k_4 = f(x_k + h, y_k + hk_3).$$

The use of this formula for the solution of our standard example is implemented in Program 6.2.1 which results in the approximation $y_{10} = 2.718\,235$ which is in error by about 5×10^{-5}—a significant improvement over the two-stage methods used earlier.

PROGRAM 6.2.1

```
10 OPEN "RESULTS." FOR OUTPUT AS FILE £3
   REM***SOLUTION OF DIFFERENTIAL EQUATION USING 4-STAGE RK FORMULA***
   REM****   TEST EQUATION IS Y' = 3X↑2*Y; Y(0) = 1 ON [0,1]   ****

20 DEF FNF(X, Y) = 3*X*X*Y
   DIM Y(10)
   X = 0 \ Y(0) = 1 \ H = 0.1
   FOR I = 1 TO 10
   Y = Y(I − 1)
   K1 = FNF(X, Y)
   F2 = FNF(X + H/2, Y + H*K1/2)
   K3 = FNF(X + H/2, Y + H*K2/2)
   K4 = FNF(X + H, Y + H*K3)
   Y(I) = Y + H*(K1 + 2*K2 + 2*K3 + K4)/6
   X = X + H
   PRINT £3, "Y("; X; ") = "; Y(I), "TRUE VALUE = "; EXP((I/10)**3)
   NEXT I

30 STOP
   END
```

The main difficulty with the Runge–Kutta methods is the control of errors. We saw in Fig. 6.1 that the error in Euler's method can build up steadily and the same is true of the higher-order methods. The problem is complicated in this situation by the fact that there are two principal sources of error—the local and global truncation errors—as well as any effect of accumulated rounding error. By the **local truncation error**, we mean that error which is introduced in the calculation of y_{k+1} because we are not solving the (modified) equation $y' = f(x, y)$, $y(x_k) = y_k$ *exactly*. The **global truncation error** incorporates both this local truncation error and the accumulated error resulting from the local truncation errors in the earlier steps. We illustrate this for the first two steps of Euler's method in Fig. 6.2.

The Runge–Kutta methods discussed here are all the same order as their

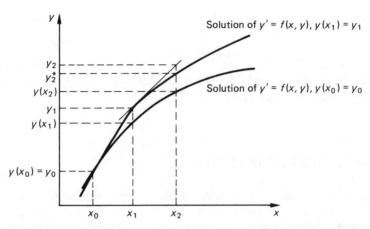

Fig. 6.2 The local truncation error in step 2 is $y_2 - y_2^*$. The global truncation error at step 2 is $y_2 - y(x_2)$.

number of stages. Thus, for example, the error in the corrected Euler formula would be expected to behave like Ch^2 for some constant C, and so halving the step length h should result in reducing the errors by a factor of about 4 whereas for the classical four-stage formula we would anticipate a reduction by a factor of about 16. There are several methods of keeping these errors under control by using a variable step length which is altered adaptively as the program progresses. The philosophy of such methods is similar to that of the adaptive quadrature methods but the detailed justification is not easy and would not be helpful at this stage. One of the most widely used of these methods is the **Runge–Kutta–Fehlberg** method, details of which can be found in, for example, the book by Yakowitz and Szidarovszky (1986).

EXERCISES 6.2

1 Repeat the calculation of Example 6.2.1(a) with $h = 0.05$ and verify that the errors have indeed been reduced by approximately the appropriate factor.

2 Modify Program 6.2.1 to implement the corrected Euler and Heun's method and to test them on the differential equation $y' = x + y^2$, $y(0) = 0$ for the interval $[0, 1]$ using the step lengths $1E - k$ for $k = 1, 2, 3$ in each case tabulating the results at $x = 0, 0.1, 0.2, \ldots, 1.0$.

3 Repeat the last exercise (Exercises 6.2, **2**) for the classical Runge–Kutta formula.

4 Show that, if $f(x, y)$ is a function of x alone, then the classical four-stage

Runge–Kutta formula is just the application of the composite Simpson's rule with subdivisions of length h.

5 Solve the equation $y' = -x \tan y$, $y(0) = \pi/6$ for $x \in [0, 1]$. Compare your solution at the points $x = k/10$ with that obtained by the classical Runge–Kutta formula using $h = 0.1$ and 0.05.

6.3 MULTISTEP METHODS

In this section, we consider methods which, like the Runge–Kutta methods, use more than just one point to calculate the estimated value of y_{k+1} but this time all the information used is taken from tabulated points. Thus again considering equation (6.6), namely

$$y_{k+1} = y_k + hy'_k + \frac{h^2 y''_k}{2} = y_k + hf(x_k, y_k) + \frac{h^2 y''_k}{2},$$

we can use the approximation

$$y''_k \approx \frac{y'(x_k) - y'(x_k - h)}{h}$$

$$\approx \frac{f(x_k, y_k) - f(x_{k-1}, y_{k-1})}{h},$$

which yields the **two-step formula**

$$y_{k+1} = y_k + hf_k + \frac{h^2 (f_k - f_{k-1})}{2h}$$

$$= y_k + \frac{h(3f_k - f_{k-1})}{2}. \tag{6.12}$$

This particular formula is an example of the Adams–Bashforth methods.

We shall consider here only the class of multistep methods known as the **Adams methods** which include the Adams–Bashforth methods as one of two important subclasses. An N-step Adams method uses a formula

$$y_{k+1} = y_k + h \sum_{j=0}^{N} \beta_j f_{k+1-j}, \tag{6.13}$$

where the coefficients β_j are chosen to give the maximum possible order of agreement with the Taylor series.

There are two fundamentally different types of the Adams method. If the coefficient β_0 in equation (6.13) is non-zero, then the value of y_{k+1} is dependent on f_{k+1}, that is, we have an *implicit* formula for y_{k+1}. Such a method is known as the **Adams–Moulton method**. The explicit formulae, such as equation (6.12) above, which are obtained with $\beta_0 = 0$ are called the **Adams–Bashforth methods**.

As an example of the Adams–Moulton methods, we consider the Taylor series approximation

$$y(x_{k+1}) \approx y_k + hy'_k + \frac{h^2 y''_k}{2} + \frac{h^3 y_k^{(3)}}{6} \tag{6.14}$$

and again use approximations for the higher-order terms. Since the Adams–Moulton formulae are implicit we can this time use the better, symmetric, approximation (cf. equation (5.25))

$$y''_k \approx \frac{y'_{k+1} - y'_{k-1}}{2h}$$

$$= \frac{f_{k+1} - f_{k-1}}{2h},$$

while, from equation (5.27), we have

$$y_k^{(3)} \approx \frac{y'_{k+1} - 2y'_k + y'_{k-1}}{h^2}$$

$$= \frac{f_{k+1} - 2f_k + f_{k-1}}{h^2}.$$

Substituting these in equation (6.14), we get

$$y_{k+1} = y_k + hf_k + \frac{h(f_{k+1} - f_{k-1})}{4} + \frac{h(f_{k+1} - 2f_k + f_{k-1})}{6}$$

$$= y_k + \frac{h(5f_{k+1} + 8f_k - f_{k-1})}{12}, \tag{6.15}$$

which is the two-step Adams–Moulton formula.

So far, we have completely ignored one major problem with these multistep methods, which is the question of how to start the process off. After all, formulae such as equations (6.12) and (6.15) for the evaluation of y_1 appear to require the value y_{-1} which is not information that is available to us. Thus these particular formulae are only of any potential use for finding $y_2, y_3, \ldots$, once y_1 has been obtained. This difficulty is increased for higher-order methods. The usual approach to this difficulty is to use a Runge–Kutta method of at least the same order as the desired multistep method to generate the values necessary to get the process started.

The Adams–Moulton methods appear to have a further difficulty inherent in their construction in that to use, say, equation (6.15) to find y_{k+1} requires the numerical solution of some implicit equation. For this reason the primary use of the Adams–Moulton formulae is in **prediction–corrector methods**. The idea behind these is that an Adams–Bashforth formulae is used to estimate the value of $y(x_{k+1})$ and this is then used in place of y_{k+1} on the right-hand side of an Adams–Moulton formula in order to obtain an improved estimate for y_{k+1}. The Adams–Bashforth method is thus used to *predict* the value y_{k+1} and the Adams–Moulton formula is the *corrector* which may be applied iteratively until convergence. Before discussing these matters in detail, we shall demonstrate one of the ways in which the coefficients of Adams formulae can be obtained.

Now, if the solution $y(x)$ is in fact a polynomial and the function $f(x, y)$ has no explicit dependence on y, then it follows that

$$y_{k+1} - y_k = \int_{x_k}^{x_{k+1}} f(x)\,dx$$

$$= \int_0^1 f(x_k + ht)h\,dt.$$

We can then seek values of the coefficients β_j so that the corresponding formula has the maximum possible degree of precision in just the same way as we did for quadrature formulae in the previous chapter. (Note here that the corresponding quadrature formulae would use integration points from outside the range of integration.)

For a three-step Adams–Bashforth formulae we thus seek β_1, β_2, β_3 so that the resulting formula is exact for all quadratics. That is, if $F(t) = f(x_k + ht) = 1,\ t,\ t^2$, we require

$$\int_0^1 F(t)\,dt = \beta_1 F(0) + \beta_2 F(-1) + \beta_3 F(-2).$$

We thus have the equations

$$F(t) = 1; \qquad \beta_1 + \beta_2 + \beta_3 = 1,$$
$$F(t) = t: \qquad -\beta_2 - 2\beta_3 = \tfrac{1}{2},$$
$$F(t) = t^2: \qquad \beta_2 + 4\beta_3 = \tfrac{1}{3}.$$

Adding the last two of these gives $\beta_3 = \tfrac{5}{12}$ and thence $\beta_2 = -\tfrac{4}{3}$ and $\beta_1 = \tfrac{23}{12}$. Thus the three-step Adams–Bashforth method uses the formula

$$y_{k+1} = y_k + \frac{h(23f_k - 16f_{k-1} + 5f_{k-2})}{12}. \tag{6.16}$$

(Note here that the sum of the coefficients is always unity which can provide a useful and simple check.)

For the corresponding three-step Adams–Moulton formula we require $\beta_0, \beta_1, \beta_2$ and β_3 such that

$$\int_0^1 F(t)\, dt = \beta_0 F(1) + \beta_1 F(0) + \beta_2 F(-1) + \beta_3 F(-2),$$

which in the same way as above yields the formula

$$y_{k+1} = y_k + \frac{h(9f_{k+1} + 19f_k - 5f_{k-1} + f_{k-2})}{24}. \qquad (6.17)$$

In the following program, we use these last two formulae as a predictor–corrector pair after the initial values y_1 and y_2 are generated by the four-stage Runge–Kutta formula (6.11). First, we see just how this operates by considering the first couple of steps in detail.

Example 6.3.1

We again consider the equation $y' = 3x^2 y$, $y(0) = 1$ using the step length $h = 0.1$.

The first two values given by the Runge–Kutta formula are

$$y_1 = 1.001\,001$$

and

$$y_2 = 1.008\,032,$$

from which the *predictor* (6.16) is used to obtain

$$y_3^p = y_2 + \frac{0.1(23f_2 - 16f_1 + 5f_0)}{12}$$

$$= 1.008\,032 + \frac{0.1(2.782\,168 - 0.480\,480 + 0)}{12}$$

$$= 1.027\,213.$$

This value can then be used to yield the value $f_3^p = f(x_3, y_3^p) = 0.277\,347$ which is then used in the right-hand side of equation (6.17) to obtain the *corrected* value

$$y_3^c = y_2 + \frac{0.1(9f_3^p + 19f_2 - 5f_1 + f_0)}{24}$$

$$= 1.008\,032 + \frac{0.1(2.496\,123 + 2.298\,313 - 0.150\,150 + 0)}{24}$$

$$= 1.027\,383,$$

which is taken as the value of y_3 for the next step. We thus get

$$y_4^p = 1.027\,383 + \frac{0.1(6.380\,048 - 1.935\,421 + 0.150\,150)}{12}$$

$$= 1.065\,673$$

and then

$$y_4^c = 1.027\,383 + \ldots$$

$$+ \frac{0.1(4.603\,707 + 5.270\,475 - 0.604\,819 + 0.030\,030)}{24}$$

$$= 1.066\,131.$$

These results compare with true values $y(0.3) = 1.027\,368$ and $y(0.4) = 1.066\,092$. The errors are slightly greater than those of the Runge–Kutta method at this stage but are obtained without any further use of non-tabular points.

PROGRAM 6.3.1

```
10 OPEN "ADAMS." FOR OUTPUT AS FILE £3
REM***SOLUTION OF DIFFERENTIAL EQUATION USING 3-STEP ADAMS FORMULAE***
REM****      AS A PREDICTOR–CORRECTOR PAIR      ****
REM***   TEST EQUATION IS Y' = 3X↑2*Y; Y(0) = 1 ON [0,1]   ***
20 DEF FNF(X, Y) = 3*X*X*Y
   DIM Y(10), F(10)
   X = 0 \ Y(0) = 1 \ H = 0.1
   FOR I = 1 TO 2
      Y = Y(I − 1) \ K1 = FNF(X, Y) \ K2 = FNF(X + H/2, Y + H*K1/2)
      K3 = FNF(X + H/2, Y + H*K2/2) \ K4 = FNF(X + H, Y + H*K3) \ X = X + H
      Y(I) = Y + H*(K1 + 2*K2 + 2*K3 + K4)/6 \ F(I − 1) = K1
      PRINT £3, "Y("; X; ") = "; Y(I)
   NEXT I
   REM***THIS USES 4-STAGE RK FORMULAE TO SET UP INITIAL VALUES***
30 F(2) = FNF(X, Y(2))
40 FOR I = 3 TO 10
      X = X + H
      YP = Y(I − 1) + H*(23*F(I − 1) − 16*F(I − 2) + 5*F(I − 3))/12
      FP = FNF(X, YP)
      Y(I) = Y(I − 1) + H*(9*FP + 19*F(I − 1) − 5*F(I − 2) + F(I − 3))/24
      F(I) = FNF(X, Y(I))
      PRINT £3, "Y("; X; ") = "; Y(I)
   NEXT I
50 STOP
   END
```

The value of $y(1)$ obtained by this program is 2.716 599, which is in error by less than 0.002, representing relatively high accuracy for little computational effort. With a smaller step length $h = 0.05$, we obtain $y(1) = 2.718\,13$, representing an improvement by a factor of about 13. This is still a considerably cheaper option than using the four-stage Runge–Kutta method with the original step length 0.1. Indeed a further halving of the Adams step length would make the two roughly equally expensive in terms of computational effort and a similar proportional improvement would lead to a final result of comparable accuracy with that obtained by the Runge–Kutta method. An alternative way of improving the accuracy of the predictor–corrector method for little extra effort would be to repeat the use of the corrector on each step.

EXERCISES 6.3

1 Derive the three-step Adams–Moulton formula (6.17).

2 Use the error formulae for the numerical differentiation formulae (5.25) and (5.27) to show that the two-step Adams–Moulton method (6.15) does indeed have a local truncation error of order h^4.

3 Modify Program 6.3.1 to use a repeated application of the corrector formula. Compare the results with those quoted in Example 6.3.1 and at the end of the program using step lengths $h = 0.1$ and 0.05.

4 Run the modified program of the last exercise (Exercises 6.3, **3**), with a step length of 0.01, printing the results at $x = 0, 0.1, 0.2, \ldots, 1.0$ and compare them with those of Exercises 6.2, **2** and **3**.

5 Tabulate the solution obtained by the three-step predictor–corrector method using $h = 0.1$, 0.05 and 0.01 for the equation $y' = -x \tan y$, $y(0) = \pi/6$ for $x \in [0, 1]$ at the points $x = k/10$. Compare these results with the true solution and the values obtained by the classical Runge–Kutta method.

6.4 SYSTEMS OF DIFFERENTIAL EQUATIONS

In this very short section, we shall consider the problem of solving a system of first-order differential equations. Such a system can be written as

$$
\begin{aligned}
y_0'(x) &= f_0(x, y_0, y_1, \ldots, y_n) & y_0(x_0) &= y_{0,0}, \\
y_1'(x) &= f_1(x, y_0, y_1, \ldots, y_n) & y_1(x_0) &= y_{1,0}, \\
y_2'(x) &= f_2(x, y_0, y_1, \ldots, y_n) & y_2(x_0) &= y_{2,0}, \qquad (6.18) \\
&\;\cdots\cdots\cdots\cdots\cdots & &\;\cdots\cdots\cdots \\
y_n'(x) &= f_n(x, y_0, y_1, \ldots, y_n) & y_n(x_0) &= y_{n,0},
\end{aligned}
$$

161

or in vector terms

$$y(x) = f(x, y) \qquad y(x_0) = y_0.$$

For any such system, we have a similar choice of available methods to that for a single initial-value problem. That is, we can proceed to find the solution in a step-by-step manner starting from $x = x_0$ and computing the approximate values of $y_1(x_1)$, $y_2(x_1)$, ..., $y_n(x_1)$ from the known initial conditions. However, a little extra care is needed since, if we are to use a Runge–Kutta method, for example, it will be necessary to compute the full vector of quantities k_1 before proceeding to any of the k_2 values and so on throughout the step. Similarly, if a predictor–corrector is to be used, it is necessary to compute the full vector of predicted values for the next step before applying any of the correctors. This process is illustrated below.

Before considering any particular case, it is important to consider one important source of systems of differential equations; higher-order differential equations are often successfully treated by recasting them as systems.

Suppose that we are given an mth-order initial-value problem

$$y^{(m)} = f(x, y, y', y'', \ldots, y^{(m-1)})$$

$$y(x_0) = y_0, y'(x_0) = y_1, \ldots, y^{(m-1)}(x_0) = y_{m-1}; \qquad (6.19)$$

then, denoting $y^{(k)}(x)$ by $y_k(x)$ for $k = 0, 1, \ldots, m-1$, we have $y'_0 = y_1$, $y'_1 = y_2, \ldots$ Thus

$$y'_k(x) = y_{k+1}(x) \qquad \text{for } k = 0, 1, \ldots, m-2$$

and $\qquad\qquad\qquad\qquad\qquad\qquad\qquad\qquad\qquad\qquad\qquad (6.20)$

$$y'_{m-1}(x) = f(x, y_0, y_1, \ldots, y_{m-1}),$$

and so we have a system of first-order initial-value problems as in equation (6.19). We illustrate this procedure and the subsequent numerical solution with a simple example.

___

Example 6.4.1

The second-order differential equation

$$y'' = 4xy' + 2(1 - 2x^2)y \qquad y(0) = 0, \ y'(0) = 1$$

is equivalent to the system

$$y'_0 = y_1 \qquad\qquad\qquad y_0(0) = 0,$$

$$y'_1 = 4xy_1 + 2(1 - 2x^2)y_0 \qquad y_1(0) = 1.$$

To simplify the description, we consider the solution of this equation using the corrected Euler formula (6.9) with $h = 0.1$. In vector terms, we then have the procedure:

$$k_1 = f(x_k, y_k),$$

$$k_2 = f\left(x_k + \frac{h}{2}, y_k + \frac{hk_1}{2}\right)$$

and then

$$y_{k+1} = y_k + hk_2.$$

Thus we find for the first step that

$$k_1 = (1, 0)^\mathrm{T},$$

$$k_2 = (1, 0.2995)^\mathrm{T}$$

and hence

$$y_1 = (0.1, 1.029\,95)^\mathrm{T}$$

the components of which are estimates of the value of the solution and its derivative at $x = 0.1$. The solution of this equation is $y(x) = x\exp(x^2)$ and so the true values are 0.101 005 and 1.030 25, respectively.

For the next step, we have

$$k_1 = (1.029\,95, 0.607\,98)^\mathrm{T},$$

$$k_2 = (1.060\,349, 0.925\,570)^\mathrm{T},$$

$$y_2 = (0.206\,035, 1.122\,507)^\mathrm{T},$$

which compares with true values $y(0.2) = 0.208\,162$ and $y'(0.2) = 1.124\,076$.

It is apparent that the only real complication introduced in the above example stems from the fact that each of the components of the right-hand side function for our numerical solution may depend on all the various components of the required solution $y(x)$. Thus the process does not lend itself to 'hand-calculation' and requires great care in its programming. There is, however, one major additional difficulty that we have to face in the case of higher-order differential equations or even sometimes with a first-order problem. This arises when the boundary conditions are not given at just one point as in the case of the initial-value problems we have considered thus far but at two or more points. We consider one approach to such *two-point boundary-value* problems in the next section.

6.5 SHOOTING METHODS

The basic philosophy behind **shooting methods** for the solution of a two-point boundary-value problem is that we embed the solution of an initial-value problem within an equation-solving routine which is then used to find the appropriate initial conditions so that the final boundary conditions are also satisfied. The solution of this initial-value problem is then the solution of the original boundary-value problem. The details will vary depending on the particular type of equation to be solved and we content ourselves here with illustrative examples.

Suppose then that we wish to solve the two-point boundary-value problem

$$y'' = f(x, y, y') \qquad y(0) = y_0 \qquad y(1) = y_1. \qquad (6.21)$$

Now the initial-value problem

$$y'' = f(x, y, y') \qquad y(0) = y_0 \qquad y'(0) = z \qquad (6.22)$$

has a solution for many values of the (as yet unknown) quantity z and for each of these there is a corresponding value of $y(1)$ which we denote by $y(1; z)$. If we can solve the equation

$$y(1; z) = y_1 \qquad (6.23)$$

for z, then it will follow that the solution of equation (6.22) for this value of z also satisfies equation (6.21).

The term shooting method derives from the fact that we try different potential values for z with the aim of finding the one which hits the *target* $y(1) = y_1$.

Equation (6.23) must be solved by some numerical technique. Now $y(1; z)$ is not a readily differentiable function of z and so the secant method is the iterative scheme which is usually adopted for this particular task.

Two-point boundary-value problems are not necessarily second-order differential equations, of course, but the underlying approach of the shooting methods is the same. We illustrate the implementation of the method with a relatively simple first-order example based on the standard test equation used earlier.

Example 6.5.1

We solve the equation $y' = 3x^2 y$, $y(0) + y(1)^2 = 3$ using a shooting method.

For any given value $y(0) = z$, say, we generate the corresponding value $y(1) = y(1; z)$, say, and must solve the equation

$$F(z) = z + y(1; z)^2 - 3 = 0.$$

The procedure is that for any z we estimate $y(1; z)$ by solving the initial-value problem

$$y' = 3x^2 y; \qquad y(0) = z$$

using the four-stage Runge–Kutta method of section 6.2 with step length

$h = 0.01$. This is then used to evaluate $F(z)$, and the equation $F(z) = 0$ is solved by the secant method.

Now, with $z = y(0) = 1$, we get $y(1; z) = 2.718\,277$ and so $F(1) = 5.389\,032$ while, with $z = y(0) = 0$, we get $y(1; z) = 0$ and $F(0) = -3$. The next value of z given by the secant iteration using $z_0 = 0$ and $z_1 = 1$ is therefore

$$z_2 = 1 - \frac{5.389\,032(1 - 0)}{5.389\,032 + 3}$$

$$= 0.357\,610,$$

from which we obtain $y(1; z_2) = 0.972\,084$ and $F(z_2) = -1.697\,443$. The next few iterations yield

$z_3 = 0.511\,483$	$y(1; z_3) = 1.390\,354$	$F(z_3) = -0.555\,433,$
$z_4 = 0.586\,322$	$y(1; z_4) = 1.593\,787$	$F(z_4) = 0.126\,478,$
$z_5 = 0.572\,441$	$y(1; z_5) = 1.556\,054$	$F(z_5) = -0.006\,254,$
$z_6 = 0.573\,095$	$y(1; z_6) = 1.557\,832$	$F(z_6) = -0.000\,064,$

which we see are settling down rapidly and providing steadily smaller values of $F(z)$.

The true solution in this case can be computed directly since $y(1) = ey(0)$ and so our equation for z becomes simply $e^2 z^2 + z^{-3} = 0$ which has its positive root at $z = 0.573\,101$ so that our shooting method has indeed produced good approximations to the required solution very quickly.

EXERCISES 6.5

1 Show that for our standard example, $y' = 3x^2 y$, we have $y(1) = ey(0)$. Suppose that the shooting method is to be used to solve this equation subject to the two-point boundary condition $y(0) + y(1) = 4$. Show that, in the absence of any numerical errors, just one secant iteration will produce the exact solution. (Notice that the resulting equation will be linear in the unknown $y(0)$ and consider the derivation of the secant method.)

2 Embed the Runge–Kutta method of Program 6.2.1 in the secant method (see Program 2.4.1) to provide a program for the solution of a first-order boundary value problem. Use this to solve $y' = -x \tan y$ on $[0, 1]$ subject to the boundary condition $y(0) + y(1) = 1$.

7 LINEAR EQUATIONS

7.1 INTRODUCTION

We have observed, in several situations, the need to be able to solve a system of linear simultaneous equations. This arose, for example, in the study of interpolation, whether by polynomials or by splines, and then in considering numerical integration. Such problems also arise naturally in direct application and in the numerical solution of systems of differential equations. We shall see later that one of the common approaches to the approximation of functions reduces to the solution of a system of linear equations.

In the case where the number of equations and the number of unknowns are both small such a system can be readily solved by hand using the familiar method of eliminating the unknowns one by one by solving one equation for one of them in terms of the others until we are left with one equation in one unknown and then substituting the solution of this back into the previous equation to find the next and so on. This is a very terse, and somewhat vague, description of the process known as **Gauss elimination** which we discuss more systematically in the next section. There are direct methods available such as Cramer's rule which for a system of N equations in N unknowns requires the evaluation of $N + 1 N \times N$ determinants. Such a determinant is defined using $N!$ products of N numbers each. Even for a 10×10 system this process therefore requires some *359 million* multiplications. This is not a task to be undertaken by hand! Nor is it a sensible way of obtaining the solution on an automatic computer.

We shall concentrate our efforts, in this brief introduction to an enormous subject, on the problem of solving a square system of equations with a single right-hand side. That is, we shall solve a system of the form

$$\mathbf{A}x = b, \tag{7.1}$$

where x and b are N vectors and $\mathbf{A}$ is an $N \times N$ real matrix, or

$$\begin{pmatrix} a_{11} & a_{12} & a_{13} & . & . & a_{1N} \\ a_{21} & a_{22} & a_{23} & . & . & a_{2N} \\ a_{31} & a_{32} & a_{33} & . & . & a_{3N} \\ . & . & . & . & . & . \\ . & . & . & . & . & . \\ a_{N1} & a_{N2} & a_{N3} & . & . & a_{NN} \end{pmatrix} \begin{pmatrix} x_1 \\ x_2 \\ x_3 \\ . \\ . \\ x_N \end{pmatrix} = \begin{pmatrix} b_1 \\ b_2 \\ b_3 \\ . \\ . \\ b_N \end{pmatrix} \qquad (7.1)'$$

or, writing the equations in full,

$$a_{11}x_1 + a_{12}x_2 + a_{13}x_3 + \ldots + a_{1N}x_N = b_1,$$

$$a_{21}x_1 + a_{22}x_2 + a_{23}x_3 + \ldots + a_{2N}x_N = b_2,$$

$$a_{31}x_1 + a_{32}x_2 + a_{33}x_3 + \ldots + a_{3N}x_N = b_3, \qquad (7.1)''$$

$$. \quad . \quad . \quad . \quad . \quad . \quad . \quad . \quad . \quad . \quad . \quad . \quad ,$$

$$a_{N1}x_1 + a_{N2}x_2 + a_{N3}x_3 + \ldots + a_{NN}x_N = b_N.$$

(Readers who are not familiar with matrix representations are referred to Towers (1988).)

There are many other situations of interest some of which can be treated by straightforward extensions of the ideas discussed in this chapter. The case of multiple right-hand sides, for example, can be handled by the methods of the next two sections with very little modification beyond the obvious requirement that whatever is done to the one right-hand-side vector must be done to them all.

One very important linear-algebra problem which we do not even attempt here is the **eigenvalue problem** which requires the solution of the equation $\mathbf{A}x = \lambda x$ for the eigenvalues λ and their associated eigenvectors x. Like most of the topics covered in this book, the numerical solution of the algebraic eigenvalue problem has been the subject of several books.

7.2 GAUSS ELIMINATION

The basic method of Gauss elimination for our system of equations $(7.1)''$ is as follows. We begin by eliminating x_1 from all but the first equation. This is achieved by subtracting from the ith equation $(i = 2, 3, \ldots, N)$ the appropriate multiple a_{i1}/a_{11} of the first equation to yield the system

$$a_{11}x_1 + a_{12}x_2 + a_{13}x_3 + \ldots + a_{1N}x_N = b_1,$$

$$a'_{22}x_2 + a'_{23}x_3 + \ldots + a'_{2N}x_N = b'_2,$$

$$a'_{32}x_2 + a'_{33}x_3 + \ldots + a'_{3N}x_N = b'_3, \qquad (7.2)''$$

$$. \quad . \quad . \quad . \quad . \quad . \quad . \quad . \quad . \quad . \quad . \quad ,$$

$$a'_{N2}x_2 + a'_{N3}x_3 + \ldots + a'_{NN}x_N = b'_N,$$

which in matrix notation is

$$
\begin{pmatrix}
a_{11} & a_{12} & a_{13} & . & . & a_{1N} \\
0 & a'_{22} & a'_{23} & . & . & a'_{2N} \\
0 & a'_{32} & a'_{33} & . & . & a'_{3N} \\
. & . & . & . & . & . \\
. & . & . & . & . & . \\
0 & a'_{N2} & a'_{N3} & . & . & a'_{NN}
\end{pmatrix}
\begin{pmatrix}
x_1 \\ x_2 \\ x_3 \\ . \\ . \\ x_N
\end{pmatrix}
=
\begin{pmatrix}
b_1 \\ b'_2 \\ b'_3 \\ . \\ . \\ b'_N
\end{pmatrix}, \qquad (7.2)'
$$

where the new coefficients are given by

$$
a'_{ij} = a_{ij} - \frac{a_{i1}a_{1j}}{a_{11}},
$$

$$
b'_i = b_i - \frac{a_{i1}b_1}{a_{11}}.
$$

$$(7.3)$$

The process continues by subtracting the appropriate multiples of the second row (or equation) from all the subsequent ones to eliminate x_2 from those equations and so on until we are left with a **triangular** system of equations.

This part of the process is known as **forward elimination**. This must be followed by the so-called **back substitution** in which we solve the final equation—which only involves x_N—and substitute this back into the previous equation which is then solved for x_{N-1} and so on until eventually we have the complete solution. What we have described here is known as *naive* Gauss elimination because we adopt the simplest approach of just taking the equations in their original order without paying any attention to the likely behaviour of the method. In the next example, we illustrate this approach and show that it can easily lead to difficulties either because the naive algorithm actually breaks down or because it can result in substantial errors. We also illustrate the method of **partial pivoting** which is often used to overcome the difficulties just mentioned.

Example 7.2.1

Consider the system of equations

$$
7x_1 + 7x_2 + x_3 = 1,
$$

$$
-4x_1 + 4x_2 - x_3 = -1,
$$

$$
7x_1 + 7x_2 - 4x_3 = 10.
$$

Suppose first that we use exact arithmetic: we begin by subtracting $-4/7$ times the first row from the second and $7/7$ times the first row from the third. This leaves the system (written in a somewhat condensed form)

$$\begin{pmatrix} 7 & -7 & 1 & 1 \\ 0 & 0 & -3/7 & -3/7 \\ 0 & 14 & -5 & 9 \end{pmatrix},$$

at which point the naive algorithm breaks down because we want to subtract $14/0$ times the second row from the third!

Of course, in this particular situation, we could simply solve the equation represented by the second row, namely $-3x_3/7 = -3/7$, to get $x_3 = 1$. We can now substitute this into the third one, $14x_2 - 5x_3 = 9$, to get $x_2 = 1$ and then the first of the equations gives us $x_1 = 1$. What we have just seen is an extreme example of the need for pivoting—and indeed that is precisely what we have just used!

To illustrate the ideas of pivoting, let us reconsider this same set of equations but this time using a hypothetical computer which works to four decimal places. The first multiplier $-4/7$ becomes -0.5714 and so the reduced system is now

$$\begin{pmatrix} 7 & -7 & 1 & 1 \\ 0 & 0.0002 & -0.4286 & -0.4286 \\ 0 & 14 & -5 & 9 \end{pmatrix}.$$

(Note here that, since the multipliers are chosen to force the entries in the first column to be zero, this value is inserted without performing the arithmetic.) The next stage of the naive Gauss elimination process is to subtract $14/0.0002 = 70\,000$ times the second row from the last to obtain the third equation $29\,997x_3 = 30\,011$. This has the solution $x_3 = 1.0005$ from which we get $x_2 = 1.0715$ and $x_1 = 1.0714$.

What is the cause of these large errors?

The entry $a'_{22} = 0.0002$ here consists solely of rounding error and this very small quantity is then used as the divisor from which we obtain the huge multiplier $70\,000$ used in the final stage of the forward elimination. As a result the value of x_3 has a small error but this is exaggerated by the subsequent division by 0.0002 in solving for x_2 in the back-substitution phase. The root cause of the errors is the repeated division by a small number which is subject to a relatively large rounding error.

If in the second stage of the elimination we had interchanged the second and third equations or rows, we would have used the larger number 14 (whose relative rounding error is likely to be small) as the divisor—or *pivot*—in determining the multiplier to be used. We thus use the system

$$\begin{pmatrix} 7 & -7 & 1 & 1 \\ 0 & 14 & -5 & 9 \\ 0 & 0.0002 & -0.4286 & -0.4286 \end{pmatrix},$$

which results in a multiplier $0.0002/14$ which is 0 to four decimal places and so yields the final equation $-0.4286x_3 = -0.4286$, giving the correct solution for x_3 and thence for x_2 and x_1. Even if we use the exact value of $0.0002/14$, we get $x_3 = 1.0005$ and then $x_2 = 1.0002$, $x_1 = 1.0001$ and so indeed the errors of the naive algorithm have been significantly reduced.

At each stage of the forward-elimination process of Gauss elimination with partial pivoting, we search for the largest coefficient *in absolute value* lying on or below the diagonal and use this as the pivot. Thus, if the current matrix at the kth stage is **B**, then we find the largest of $|b_{kk}|, |b_{k+1k}|, \ldots, |b_{Nk}|$. The corresponding row is then interchanged with the kth one and the elimination proceeds using the appropriate pivot. This is incorporated into the following program.

PROGRAM 7.2.1

```
1       OPEN "GAUSS.LIS" FOR OUTPUT AS FILE £3
        REM****SOLUTION OF LINEAR EQUATIONS BY****
        REM***GAUSS ELIMINATION WITH PARTIAL PIVOTING***
10      DIM A(10,10),B(10),X(10)
        READ N
        PRINT £3, "ORIGINAL SYSTEM"
        FOR I = 1 TO N
          FOR J = 1 TO N \ READ A(I,J) \ PRINT £3, A(I,J);"   "; \ NEXT J
        READ B(I) \ PRINT £3, B(I)
15      NEXT I

        REM****BEGIN FORWARD ELIMINATION****
20      FOR I = 1 TO N − 1
        REM****FIND PIVOT ROW****
21        P = I \ PIVOT = ABS(A(I,I))
          FOR K = I + 1 TO N
            IF ABS(A(K,I)) > PIVOT THEN P = K \ PIVOT = ABS(A(K,I))
25        NEXT K
        REM*** ROW P IS PIVOTAL ROW; INTERCHANGE WITH ROW I IF NECESSARY***
26        IF P = I THEN 30
27          FOR J = I TO N \ A(0,J) = A(I,J) \ A(I,J) = A(P,J) \ A(P,J) = A(0,J) \ NEXT J
            B(0) = B(I) \ B(I) = B(P) \ B(P) = B(0)
        REM***INTERCHANGE COMPLETE; START ELIMINATION***

30        FOR K = I + 1 TO N
            MULT = A(K,I)/A(I,I) \ A(K,I) = 0
            FOR J = I + 1 TO N \ A(K,J) = A(K,J) − MULT*A(I,J) \ NEXT J
            B(K) = B(K) − MULT*B(I)
          NEXT K
40      NEXT I

        REM***FORWARD ELIMINATION COMPLETE***
45      PRINT £3, \ PRINT £3,"TRIANGULAR SYSTEM IS" \ PRINT £3,
        FOR I = 1 TO N
          FOR J = 1 TO N \ PRINT £3,A(I,J);"   "; \ NEXT J \ PRINT £3,B(I)
        NEXT I

        REM***START BACKWARD SUBSTITUTION***
50      PRINT £3,"SOLUTION" \ PRINT £3,
        X(N) = B(N)/A(N,N) \ PRINT £3,"X(";N;") = ";X(N)
```

```
      FOR K = 1 TO N − 1
        FOR J = N − K + 1 TO N \ B(N − K) = B(N − K) − A(N − K,J)*X(J) \ NEXT J
        X(N − K) = B(N − K)/A(N − K,N − K) \ PRINT £3,"X(";N − K;") = ";X(N − K)
55    NEXT K
60    STOP

80    DATA 5
      DATA 1,2,3,4,5,15
      DATA 2,2,3,4,5,16
      DATA 3,3,3,4,5,18
      DATA 4,4,4,4,5,21
      DATA 5,5,5,5,5,25

100   END
```

This program produces the output:

ORIGINAL SYSTEM

1	2	3	4	5	15
2	2	3	4	5	16
3	3	3	4	5	18
4	4	4	4	5	21
5	5	5	5	5	25

TRIANGULAR SYSTEM IS

5	5	5	5	5	25
0	1	2	3	4	10
0	0	1	2	3	6
0	0	0	1	2	3
0	0	0	0	1	1

RESULTS
$X(5) = 1$
$X(4) = 1$
$X(3) = 1$
$X(2) = 1$
$X(1) = 1$

which is of course the exact solution of this very simple system.

The original system here is very *well conditioned*, which is to say that the solution is not highly sensitive to small changes in the data or, almost equivalently, to rounding errors. Determining whether or not a particular system is well conditioned is beyond the scope of the present work; it relies on the ability to estimate the ratio of the largest to smallest eigenvalues of the original matrix.

Before leaving Gauss elimination, there are a few remarks to make on the above program. Firstly, there is no test incorporated for the possible singularity of the matrix of coefficients; such a test would be an essential part of any decent software package. Not only is it necessary to test whether the

171

matrix is singular, but also we must check whether it is *almost* singular, which would often be achieved by including a test on the size of the pivot elements. Such safeguards are necessary to ensure that the answers provided are meaningful. Most commercial packages would also include the possibility of multiple right-hand sides so that many such systems with the same coefficient matrix could be solved simultaneously. This feature can also be used to provide empirical evidence of the condition of the matrix by solving the system with a right-hand side for which the exact solution is already known by taking $b_i = a_{i1} + a_{i2} + \ldots + a_{iN}$ so that $x_i = 1$ for every i, for example.

In Program 7.2.1 the row interchanges are performed explicitly but this is not absolutely necessary. We can obviate the need for this by storing a **permutation vector** $P(I)$ which is used to keep a record of the order in which the rows are used. This vector is initialised so that $P(I) = I$ for every I and then if row K is to be used as the pivotal one for the Ith stage we set $P(I) = P(K)$ and $P(K) = P(I)$ and simply replace A(I,J), A(K,J), B(I) and B(K) by A(P(I),J), A(P(K),J), B(P(I)) and B(P(K)) throughout the subsequent parts of the program.

For the special case of a tridiagonal system of equations such as those obtained in spline interpolation, it would be undesirable to 'fill up' any of the entries which are already zero and so pivoting is not usually advisable in such situations. Note too that for such a system it is wasteful to store the complete matrix and to perform arithmetic with it since many of the calculations will be of the form $0 - 0 \times a_{ii}$. For such sparse systems, it is sensible therefore to modify the Gauss elimination approach to take full account of the special structure of the system, although account must also be taken of any ill-conditioning.

Recall from our introductory remarks that using Cramer's rule the complete solution of an $N \times N$ system requires some $(N + 1)! \times (N - 1)$ multiplications; the corresponding number of multiplications and divisions for the above Gauss elimination program is about $N^3/3 + N^2/2$—quite a saving even for moderate values of N. In discussing such operation counts, it is necessary nowadays to bear in mind the possibilities that are opened up by the availability of parallel processing. On a modern supercomputer most of the operations in the above program can be **vectorised** so that effectively we operate on all the elements of a vector simultaneously. In such a situation, it would almost certainly be beneficial to eliminate both *below* and *above* the diagonal at the same time. We could thus remove the backward substitution entirely, leaving us with just N divisions to obtain the solution—and these could be performed *simultaneously* too. This process, which we do not discuss in any further detail, is known as the **Gauss–Jordan method.**

EXERCISES 7.2

1 Use Program 7.2.1 to solve the system of equations $\mathbf{A}x = b$ where $a_{ij} = 1/(i + j - 1)$ and $b_i = a_{i1} + a_{i2} + \ldots + a_{iN}$ for $N = 2, 3, \ldots, 10$. Note

that in all cases the exact solution is $x_1 = x_2 = \ldots = x_{10} = 1$ but the computed solution gets less accurate as N increases. (The matrix here is known as the **Hilbert matrix** and is notoriously ill-conditioned.)

2 Modify Program 7.2.1 so that no pivoting is performed and repeat the above exercise (Exercises 7.2, **1**). Note how the errors start to grow for smaller values of N.

3 If you have access to double-precision calculation on your computer, repeat the previous exercises (Exercises 7.2, **1** and **2**) using this facility and note how much more stable the process becomes.

4 Show, by constructing an example, that interchanging two rows of a tridiagonal system can result in filling in some of the zero entries. Try to modify the Gauss elimination procedure for the special case of the tridiagonal system (4.27) obtained for cubic spline interpolation at equally spaced points.

7.3 LU FACTORISATION; ITERATIVE REFINEMENT

One of the difficulties with the Gauss elimination approach to the solution of linear equations lies in control of the accumulation of rounding error. We saw in the last section that the use of pivoting can improve matters but even then, if the system is ill-conditioned, large relative errors can result.

It is often helpful to look at the vector of **residuals**, denoted r, whose components are given by

$$r_1 = b_1 - (a_{11}x_1 + a_{12}x_2 + \ldots + a_{1N}x_N),$$
$$r_2 = b_2 - (a_{21}x_1 + a_{22}x_2 + \ldots + a_{2N}x_N),$$
$$\cdots \cdots \cdots \cdots \cdots \cdots \cdots , \qquad (7.4)$$
$$r_N = b_N - (a_{N1}x_1 + a_{N2}x_2 + \ldots + a_{NN}x_N),$$

which provide a measure (although not always a very good one) of the extent to which we have failed to satisfy the equations. Now, if we can also solve the system of equations $Ay = r$, then, by adding this solution y to our computed solution x, say, we obtain

$$A(x + y) = Ax + Ay$$
$$= Ax + r$$
$$= Ax + b - Ax$$
$$= b, \qquad (7.5)$$

so that, if we can compute r and solve this second system *exactly*, then $x + y$ is the exact solution of our original system; we would certainly anticipate that it should be an improved solution. This suggests a possible iterative method for improving the original Gauss elimination solution of a system of linear equations.

We suggested at the end of the discussion on Gauss elimination that it is possible to solve several systems simultaneously but, of course, we do not know the *residuals* until after the original Gauss elimination is complete. It is necessary therefore to keep a record of the multipliers used in the elimination step—but we can do better than that. Consider again the first stage of the naive Gauss elimination process.

Denote the multipliers a_{i1}/a_{11} by m_{i1}. Then we find that

$$
\mathbf{A} =
\begin{pmatrix}
1 & 0 & . & . & . & . & 0 \\
m_{21} & 1 & 0 & . & . & . & 0 \\
m_{31} & 0 & 1 & 0 & . & . & 0 \\
. & . & . & . & . & . & . \\
. & . & . & . & . & . & . \\
m_{N1} & 0 & 0 & . & . & 0 & 1
\end{pmatrix}
\begin{pmatrix}
a_{11} & a_{12} & a_{13} & . & . & a_{1N} \\
0 & a'_{22} & a'_{23} & . & . & a'_{2N} \\
0 & a'_{32} & a'_{33} & . & . & a'_{3N} \\
. & . & . & . & . & . \\
. & . & . & . & . & . \\
0 & a'_{N2} & a'_{N3} & . & . & a'_{NN}
\end{pmatrix},
$$

(7.6)

since from equations (7.3) we have $a'_{ij} = a_{ij} - m_{i1}a_{1j}$ and so $a_{ij} = a'_{ij} + m_{i1}a_{1j}$. In the same way the second step uses the multipliers $m_{i2} = a'_{i2}/a'_{22}$ and we find that

$$
\mathbf{A} =
\begin{pmatrix}
1 & 0 & . & . & . & . & 0 \\
m_{21} & 1 & 0 & . & . & . & 0 \\
m_{31} & 0 & 1 & 0 & . & . & 0 \\
. & . & . & . & . & . & . \\
. & . & . & . & . & . & . \\
m_{N1} & 0 & 0 & . & . & 0 & 1
\end{pmatrix}
\begin{pmatrix}
1 & 0 & . & . & . & . & 0 \\
0 & 1 & 0 & . & . & . & 0 \\
0 & m_{32} & 1 & 0 & . & . & 0 \\
. & . & . & . & . & . & . \\
. & . & . & . & . & . & . \\
0 & m_{N2} & 0 & . & . & 0 & 1
\end{pmatrix}
\begin{pmatrix}
a_{11} & a_{12} & a_{13} & . & . & a_{1N} \\
0 & a'_{22} & a'_{23} & . & . & a'_{2N} \\
0 & 0 & a''_{33} & . & . & a''_{3N} \\
. & . & . & . & . & . \\
. & . & . & . & . & . \\
0 & 0 & a''_{N3} & . & . & a''_{NN}
\end{pmatrix}
$$

$$
=
\begin{pmatrix}
1 & 0 & . & . & . & . & 0 \\
m_{21} & 1 & 0 & . & . & . & 0 \\
m_{31} & m_{32} & 1 & 0 & . & . & 0 \\
. & . & . & . & . & . & . \\
. & . & . & . & . & . & . \\
m_{N1} & m_{N2} & 0 & . & . & 0 & 1
\end{pmatrix}
\begin{pmatrix}
a_{11} & a_{12} & a_{13} & . & . & a_{1N} \\
0 & a'_{22} & a'_{23} & . & . & a'_{2N} \\
0 & 0 & a''_{33} & . & . & a''_{3N} \\
. & . & . & . & . & . \\
. & . & . & . & . & . \\
0 & 0 & a''_{N3} & . & . & a''_{NN}
\end{pmatrix}.
$$

(7.7)

We see here that the original matrix is being broken down step by step into two factors one of which is lower triangular with unit diagonal entries while the other is upper triangular. Eventually we thus obtain

$$\mathbf{A} = \mathbf{LU}, \tag{7.8}$$

where $\mathbf{L}$ is the lower triangular factor and $\mathbf{U}$ the upper one.

This particular factorisation is known as the **Dolittle reduction**. The corresponding factorisation in which the upper triangular factor has the unit diagonal is the **Crout reduction**. Note that whichever of these is being used we can store the factors in the same memory locations in the computer as the original matrix $\mathbf{A}$; we must of course take account of the unit diagonal entries which would not be stored explicitly. (There are slightly more direct ways of computing the factors but they are necessarily equivalent to what we have described above and add little to the understanding of the process at this level.)

Returning to the problem of solving a system of linear equations, suppose now that we have our matrix $\mathbf{A}$ of coefficients factorised as $\mathbf{LU}$ so that we now wish to solve $\mathbf{LU}x = b$. If we first solve $\mathbf{L}z = b$ and then $\mathbf{U}x = z$, we obtain

$$\mathbf{A}x = \mathbf{LU}x = \mathbf{L}z = b \tag{7.9}$$

as required. Now the solution of $\mathbf{L}z = b$ can be achieved by a forward-substitution routine similar to the backward substitution used in Gauss elimination and the backward substitution can then be used to solve $\mathbf{U}x = z$.

Our motivation for studying this approach was the desire to improve our numerical solution iteratively by solving another system of equations with the residual vector of our computed solution as the right-hand side. This process is called **iterative refinement**. Having obtained our computed solution x, we can multiply this by the original matrix $\mathbf{A}$ and subtract the result from b to obtain the residual vector r. We then compute the solution z' of $\mathbf{L}z = r$ and thence the solution y of $\mathbf{U}y = z'$ or, equivalently, $\mathbf{A}y = r$, from which we obtain the improved solution (of the original equations) $x + y$. This can be repeated as often as required to obtain convergence. The great advantage of the $\mathbf{LU}$ factorisation lies in the fact that we do not need to repeat all the work of the elimination phase for the new right-hand side vector.

Example 7.3.1

Solve the equations of Example 7.2.1 using the $\mathbf{LU}$ factorisation and iterative refinement.

From the multipliers found in the earlier example, we obtain the factorisation

$$
\begin{pmatrix} 7 & -7 & 1 \\ -4 & 7 & -1 \\ 7 & 7 & -4 \end{pmatrix} = \begin{pmatrix} 0 & 0 & 0 \\ -0.5714 & 1 & 0 \\ 1 & 70000 & 1 \end{pmatrix} \begin{pmatrix} 7 & -7 & 1 \\ 0 & 0.0002 & -0.4286 \\ 0 & 0 & 29997 \end{pmatrix}
$$

and solving $\mathbf{L}z = (1, -1, 10)^T$ gives $z_1 = 1$, $z_2 = -0.4286$, $z_3 = 300\,11$ and hence the solution $x_1 = 1.0714$, $x_2 = 1.0715$, $x_3 = 1.0005$ as before. (Note that these are the multipliers and solutions obtained *without pivoting*.)

The residuals are therefore given by

$$r_1 = 1 - 7 \times 1.0714 + 7 \times 1.0715 - 1 \times 1.0005$$

$$= \quad 0.0002,$$

$$r_2 = -1 + 4 \times 1.0714 - 4 \times 1.0715 + 1 \times 1.0005$$

$$= \quad 0.0001,$$

$$r_3 = 10 - 7 \times 1.0714 - 7 \times 1.0715 + 4 \times 1.0005$$

$$= -0.9983.$$

Solving $\mathbf{L}z = r$ gives $z_1 = 0.0002$, $z_2 = 0.0002$, $z_3 = -15.9981$ still working to four decimal places and then, solving $\mathbf{U}y = z$, we get $y_3 = -0.0005$, $y_2 = -0.0715$, $y_1 = -0.0715$ so that the improved solution is $x + y = (0.9999, 1.0000, 1.0000)^T$ and we see that, despite the absence of pivoting, we have obtained a very accurate solution.

It should be observed that similar accuracy would probably have been achieved here by the use of pivoting in the original solution. As a general rule, little benefit is to be gained by iterative refinement (compared with pivoting) for a well-conditioned system unless the residuals are computed to greater precision. In the following program, iterative refinement *and* pivoting are used for a 5×5 system of equations using just a single iterative refinement which re-uses the forward- and backward-substitution code of the original solution. The pivoting is achieved using the permutation vector P(I) as outlined in the remarks following Program 7.2.1.

PROGRAM 7.3.1

1   OPEN "LU.LIS" FOR OUTPUT AS FILE £3

```
10    DIM A(10,10),A1(10,10),B(10),B1(10),X(10),Y(10),Z(10),P(I)
      READ N
      PRINT £3,"ORIGINAL SYSTEM"
      FOR I = 1 TO N
        P(I) = I
        FOR J = 1 TO N
          READ A(I,J) \ A1(I,J) = A(I,J) \ PRINT £3,A(I,J);"  ";
        NEXT J
        READ B(I) \ B1(I) = B(I) \ PRINT £3,B(I) \ X(I) = 0
      NEXT I

14    REM***LU FACTORISATION***
15    P = I \ PIVOT = ABS(A(P(I),I))
      FOR K = I + 1 TO N
        IF ABS(A(P(K),I)) > PIVOT THEN P = K \ PIVOT = ABS(A(P(K),I))
      NEXT K
      P(I) = P \ P(P) = I
20    FOR I = 1 TO N − 1
        FOR K = I + 1 TO N \ A(P(K),I) = A(P(K),I)/A(P(I),I)
          FOR J = I + 1 TO N \ A(P(K),J) = A(P(K),J) − A(P(K),I)*A(P(I),J) \ NEXT J
        NEXT K
      NEXT I
25    PRINT £3, \ PRINT £3,"TRIANGULAR FACTORS"
      FOR I = 1 TO N
        FOR J = 1 TO I − 1 \ PRINT £3,A(P(I),J);"  "; \ NEXT J \ PRINT £3,"1        ";
        FOR J = I TO N \ PRINT £3,A(P(I),J);"  "; \ NEXT J \ PRINT £3,
      NEXT I \ PRINT £3,

29    FOR M = 1 TO 2
      REM***FORWARD SUBSTITUTION***
30    Z(1) = B(P(1))
      FOR I = 2 TO N
        FOR J = 1 TO I − 1 \ B(P(I)) = B(P(I)) − A(P(I),J)*Z(J) \ NEXT J
        Z(I) = B(P(I))
      NEXT I

34    REM***BACKWARD SUBSTITUTION***
35    Y(N) = Z(N)/A(P(N),N)
      FOR K = 1 TO N − 1
        FOR J = N − K + 1 TO N \ Z(N − K) = Z(N − K) − A(P(N − K),J)*Y(J) \ NEXT J
        Y(N − K) = Z(N − K)/A(P(N − K),N − K)
      NEXT K
      PRINT £3,"SOLUTION ";M
      FOR I = 1 TO N \ X(I) = X(I) + Y(I) \ PRINT £3,"X(";I;") = ";X(I) \ NEXT I

39    REM***COMPUTE RESIDUALS***
40      FOR I = 1 TO N \ B(I) = B1(I)
          FOR J = 1 TO N \ B(I) = B(I) − A1(I,J)*X(J) \ NEXT J
        NEXT I
45    NEXT M

50    STOP
101   DATA 5,1,1,1,1,1,0.1,1,2,3,4,5,0.3,1,4,9,16,25,1.5
102   DATA 1,8,27,64,125,8,1,1,16,81,256,625,43.5
150   END
```

The true solution of this system is $x_1 = x_3 = x_5 = 0.1$ and $x_2 = x_4 = -0.1$. The triangular factors are printed as

1			1	1	1	1	1
1	1			15	80	255	624
1	0.466 666 7	1		−11.333 33	−56	−167.2
1	0.2	0.705 882 4	1		3.529 415	17.223 55
1	0.066 666 67	0.294 117 7	0.7	1		−0.480 007 2

where the extended space indicates the change from the lower to the upper triangle. The solutions obtained are, first,

$$x_1 = \quad 0.099\,997\,87,$$

$$x_2 = -0.099\,993\,39,$$

$$x_3 = \quad 0.099\,992\,09,$$

$$x_4 = -0.099\,995\,64,$$

$$x_5 = \quad 0.099\,999\,08,$$

and, after the iterative refinement,

$$x_1 = \quad 0.099\,999\,49,$$

$$x_2 = -0.099\,998\,31,$$

$$x_3 = \quad 0.099\,997\,84,$$

$$x_4 = -0.099\,998\,75,$$

$$x_5 = \quad 0.099\,999\,73,$$

which shows a significant improvement in each component despite the fact that for this example the residuals are computed in single precision.

EXERCISES 7.3

1 Modify Program 7.3.1 to perform more iterations of the refinement. How many are needed to achieve full machine accuracy for that example?

2 Apply the method of **LU** factorisation with iterative refinement to the equations of Exercises 7.2, **1**. Repeat this using double-precision arithmetic.

7.4 ITERATIVE METHODS

In this section, we again consider the system (7.1). In the situation where the number of equations is large, the computational effort required by Gauss elimination or by the **LU** factorisation approaches is still very large and alternative approaches are desirable. Amongst these are the iterative methods which we discuss here. On the assumption that $a_{ii} \neq 0$ for each i, the system

(7.1) can be rewritten as

$$x_1 = \frac{b_1 - a_{12}x_2 - a_{13}x_3 - \ldots - a_{1N}x_N}{a_{11}},$$

$$x_2 = \frac{b_2 - a_{21}x_1 - a_{23}x_3 - \ldots - a_{2N}x_N}{a_{22}}, \qquad (7.10)$$

$$\cdot \quad \cdot \quad \cdot \quad \cdot \quad \cdot \quad \cdot \quad \cdot \quad \cdot \quad \cdot \quad ,$$

$$x_N = \frac{b_N - a_{N1}x_1 - a_{N2}x_2 - \ldots - a_{NN-1}x_{N-1}}{a_{NN}},$$

which lends itself to an iterative treatment.

For the **Jacobi iteration** we simply generate the next estimated solution from the current one by substituting the current set of values $x_1, x_2, \ldots, x_N$ in the right-hand side of equations (7.10) to obtain the next iterates $x_1', x_2', \ldots, x_N'$. Thus we set

$$x_1' = \frac{b_1 - a_{12}x_2 - a_{13}x_3 - \ldots - a_{1N}x_N}{a_{11}},$$

$$x_2' = \frac{b_2 - a_{21}x_1 - a_{23}x_3 - \ldots - a_{2N}x_N}{a_{22}}, \qquad (7.11)$$

$$\cdot \quad \cdot \quad \cdot \quad \cdot \quad \cdot \quad \cdot \quad \cdot \quad \cdot \quad \cdot \quad ,$$

$$x_N' = \frac{b_N - a_{N1}x_1 - a_{N2}x_2 - \ldots - a_{NN-1}x_{N-1}}{a_{NN}}.$$

(Any specific mention of the iteration number has been omitted to simplify the notation.)

One obvious question which arises here is, once x_1' has been obtained in the first equation of (7.11), why not use it in the equation for x_2'? Similarly, we could use x_2' in the next equation for x_3' and so on throughout the system. The iterative process using this approach is the **Gauss–Seidel** iteration:

$$x_1' = \frac{b_1 - a_{12}x_2 - a_{13}x_3 - \ldots - a_{1N}x_N}{a_{11}},$$

$$x_2' = \frac{b_2 - a_{21}x_1' - a_{23}x_3 - \ldots - a_{2N}x_N}{a_{22}}, \qquad (7.12)$$

$$\cdot \quad \cdot \quad \cdot \quad \cdot \quad \cdot \quad \cdot \quad \cdot \quad \cdot \quad \cdot \quad ,$$

$$x_N' = \frac{b_N - a_{N1}x_1' - a_{N2}x_2' - \ldots - a_{NN-1}x_{N-1}'}{a_{NN}}.$$

For either of these iterative schemes a complete iteration requires N^2 multiplications and N divisions and so, if convergence is likely to be achieved in less than $N/3$ iterations, these techniques will be less expensive than Gauss elimination. This observation raises the question of the conditions under which an iterative scheme such as these will converge. A detailed study of this question is beyond the scope of this book but we can get a feel for the situation from examples.

Example 7.4.1

Consider the system of equations derived in Example 4.4.2 for fitting a cubic spline to data from the square-root function, namely

$$48c_1 + 13c_2 \qquad = -0.0420,$$
$$13c_1 + 56c_2 + 15c_3 = -0.0306,$$
$$15c_2 + 64c_3 = -0.0237.$$

Rearranging these, we obtain

$$c_1 = \frac{-0.0420 - 13c_2}{48},$$

$$c_2 = \frac{-0.0306 - 13c_1 - 15c_3}{56},$$

$$c_3 = \frac{-0.0237 - 15c_2}{64}.$$

Taking the initial guess $c_1 = c_2 = c_3 = 0$, we obtain the next estimates using a Jacobi iteration

$$c_1 = \frac{-0.0420}{48} = -0.875 \times 10^{-3},$$

$$c_2 = \frac{-0.0306}{56} = -0.546 \times 10^{-3}$$

$$c_3 = -0.370 \times 10^{-3}.$$

The next two iterations yield

$$c_1 = -0.727 \times 10^{-3} \qquad c_2 = -0.244 \times 10^{-3} \qquad c_3 = -0.362 \times 10^{-3},$$
$$c_1 = -0.809 \times 10^{-3} \qquad c_2 = -0.281 \times 10^{-3} \qquad c_3 = -0.313 \times 10^{-3},$$

which is steadily approaching the true solution $(-0.799, -0.279, -0.305) \times 10^{-3}$.

Using the Gauss–Seidel iteration, with the same starting values, the first three iterations yield

$$c_1 = -0.875 \times 10^{-3} \qquad c_2 = -0.343 \times 10^{-3} \qquad c_3 = -0.290 \times 10^{-3},$$

$$c_1 = -0.782 \times 10^{-3} \qquad c_2 = -0.259 \times 10^{-3} \qquad c_3 = -0.310 \times 10^{-3},$$

$$c_1 = -0.805 \times 10^{-3} \qquad c_2 = -0.277 \times 10^{-3} \qquad c_3 = -0.305 \times 10^{-3},$$

which for the same computational effort is much closer to the true solution.

To see that the behaviour is not always this impressive, consider the same system of equations but with the first two interchanged:

$$13c_1 + 56c_2 + 15c_3 = -0.0306,$$

$$48c_1 + 13c_2 \qquad\quad = -0.0420,$$

$$15c_2 + 64c_3 = -0.0237.$$

Again using the Gauss–Seidel iteration, we get on the first two iterations

$$c_1 = -0.235 \times 10^{-2} \qquad c_2 = 0.545 \times 10^{-2} \qquad c_3 = -0.165 \times 10^{-2},$$

$$c_1 = -0.239 \times 10^{-1} \qquad c_2 = 0.851 \times 10^{-1} \qquad c_3 = -0.203 \times 10^{-1},$$

which is clearly moving rapidly *away* from the true solution.

The crucial difference between these two systems lies in the fact that the original version in **diagonally dominant**, that is, for each row of the coefficient matrix we have

$$|a_{ii}| > \sum_{j \neq i} |a_{ij}|,$$

and the simplest condition under which these iterations will converge is that the matrix of coefficients is diagonally dominant. In the reordered system the matrix is not diagonally dominant since $a_{11} = 13 < a_{21} + a_{31} = 71$ and $a_{22} < a_{21}$.

The more rapid convergence of the Gauss–Seidel iteration in the above example is by no means universal although it is more common than not. However it should be pointed out that the Gauss–Seidel iteration would not be so useful on a parallel computer where all the computation of a Jacobi iteration could be performed simultaneously whereas for Gauss–Seidel x_2' cannot be computed until after x_1' is known.

One reason for using this particular example is that spline interpolation will typically require the solution of a large, banded, *diagonally dominant* system of equations which is therefore well suited to iterative solution. The sparsity of these banded—tridiagonal, for cubic splines—systems also means that the number of arithmetic operations per iteration is reduced and so makes the iterative solution yet more attractive.

EXERCISE 7.4

1 Write programs to solve the system of equations (4.27) for cubic spline interpolation with equally spaced data points by the Jacobi and Gauss–Seidel iterations. Test it by finding the natural cubic spline which agrees with the function $\ln x$ at $x = 1, 2, 3, 4, 5, 6, 7, 8, 9, 10$.

7.5 LINEAR LEAST-SQUARES APPROXIMATION

In this final section, we return to one of the major themes of the whole book, namely the approximation of functions. In chapter 4, we pointed out some of the potential drawbacks of polynomial interpolation in the situation where the number of data points is large and the data are perhaps subject to experimental errors. In such cases, interpolation merely forces the approximating function to reproduce these experimental errors. The approach that we study here is least-squares approximation in which we seek to find an approximating function p, say, from some particular class such that the least-squares measure of the error is minimised.

Recall from section 1.3 that the continuous L_2, or **least-squares, metric** is defined for the interval $[a, b]$ by

$$L_2(f, p) = \| f - p \|_2$$

$$= \left(\int_a^b |f(x) - p(x)|^2 \, dx \right)^{1/2} \qquad (7.13)$$

and the continuous least-squares approximation problem is to find the function p from the admissible set which minimises this quantity. Similarly, if we are given values of the function f at points x_i, $i = 0, 1, 2, \ldots, N$, the **discrete least-squares** metric is defined by

$$D_2(f, p) = \left(\sum_{i=0}^{N} |f(x_i) - p(x_i)|^2 \right)^{1/2} \qquad (7.14)$$

and the discrete least-squares problem is to find the function p, again from some specified admissible class, which minimises this measure of the error.

Clearly, one of the most important questions which must be settled here is within which class of functions we seek our approximation p. Initially, we shall consider the case of polynomial approximation so that we seek a polynomial of degree no more than M say such that $L_2(f, p)$ or $D_2(f, p)$ is minimised. Thus we must find the coefficients $a_0, a_1, a_2, \ldots, a_M$ of the polynomial p which is given by

$$p(x) = a_0 + a_1 x + a_2 x^2 + \ldots + a_M x^M. \qquad (7.15)$$

Consider first the continuous case and denote $[L_2(f, p)]^2$ by $F(a_0, a_1, \ldots, a_M)$.

The values $a_0, a_1, \ldots, a_M$ which minimise $F(a_0, a_1, \ldots, a_M)$ also minimise $L_2(f, p)$ and

$$F(a_0, a_1, \ldots, a_M) = \int_a^b [f(x) - a_0 - a_1 x - a_2 x^2 - \ldots - a_M x^M]^2 \, dx.$$

(7.16)

Now, differentiating F with respect to each of the parameters $a_0, a_1, \ldots, a_M$ and setting these partial derivatives to zero, we get the system of linear equations

$$\frac{\partial F}{\partial a_0} = \int_a^b -2[f(x) - a_0 - a_1 x - a_2 x^2 - \ldots - a_M x^M] \quad dx = 0,$$

$$\frac{\partial F}{\partial a_1} = \int_a^b -2x[f(x) - a_0 - a_1 x - a_2 x^2 - \ldots - a_M x^M] \quad dx = 0,$$

$$\cdot \quad \cdot \quad \cdot \quad \cdot \quad \cdot \quad \cdot \quad \cdot \quad \cdot \quad \cdot \quad \cdot \quad \cdot \quad \cdot \quad \cdot \quad \cdot \quad \cdot \quad \cdot \quad ,$$

$$\frac{\partial F}{\partial a_M} = \int_a^b -2x^M [f(x) - a_0 - a_1 x - a_2 x^2 - \ldots - a_M x^M] \, dx = 0,$$

which we can rewrite, on dividing by 2 and simplifying the notation, as

$$c_0 a_0 + c_1 a_1 + \ldots + c_M a_M = b_0,$$
$$c_1 a_0 + c_2 a_1 + \ldots + c_{M+1} a_M = b_1,$$
$$c_2 a_0 + c_3 a_1 + \ldots + c_{M+2} a_M = b_2,$$
$$\cdot \quad \cdot \quad \cdot \quad \cdot \quad \cdot \quad \cdot \quad \cdot \quad \cdot \quad \cdot \quad \cdot \quad ,$$
$$c_M a_0 + c_{M+1} a_1 + \ldots + c_{2M} a_M = b_M,$$

where

$$c_k = \int_a^b x^k \, dx \qquad k = 0, 1, \ldots, 2M$$

and

$$b_k = \int_a^b x^k f(x) \, dx \qquad k = 0, 1, \ldots, M.$$

For the discrete case, we obtain a similar system of linear equations with

$$c_k = \sum_{i=0}^{N} x_i^k \qquad k = 0, 1, \ldots, 2M$$

and

$$b_k = \sum_{i=0}^{N} x_i^k f(x_i) \qquad k = 0, 1, \ldots, M.$$

In either case therefore the least-squares approximation problem has been reduced to the solution of a system of linear equations, which are called the **normal equations**. The matrix of coefficients of such a system is non-singular and so there is a unique solution to our approximation problem. The reason for the name *linear* least-squares approximation is that the approximating function here is a *linear* combination of the basis functions $1, x, x^2, \ldots, x^M$.

Example 7.5.1

Find the continuous least-squares cubic approximation to $\sin x$ on the interval $[0, \pi]$.

Here we must minimise

$$\int_0^\pi (\sin x - a_0 - a_1 x - a_2 x^2 - a_3 x^3)^2 \, dx.$$

Now the coefficients c_k are given by

$$\int_0^\pi x^k \, dx = \frac{\pi^{k+1}}{k+1} \qquad k = 0, 1, \ldots, 6,$$

while

$$b_k = \int_0^\pi x^k \sin x \, dx$$

so that $b_0 = 2$, $b_1 = \pi$, $b_2 = \pi^2 - 4$ and $b_3 = \pi^3 - 6\pi$. The normal equations are thus

$$\pi a_0 + \frac{\pi^2 a_1}{2} + \frac{\pi^3 a_2}{3} + \frac{\pi^4 a_3}{4} = 2,$$

$$\frac{\pi^2 a_0}{2} + \frac{\pi^3 a_1}{3} + \frac{\pi^4 a_2}{4} + \frac{\pi^5 a_3}{5} = \pi,$$

$$\frac{\pi^3 a_0}{3} + \frac{\pi^4 a_1}{4} + \frac{\pi^5 a_2}{5} + \frac{\pi^6 a_3}{6} = \pi^2 - 4,$$

$$\frac{\pi^4 a_0}{4} + \frac{\pi^5 a_1}{5} + \frac{\pi^6 a_2}{6} + \frac{\pi^7 a_3}{7} = \pi^3 - 6\pi,$$

and, putting these values into the Gauss elimination program, Program 7.2.1, we obtain the solution $a_0 = -0.050\,469$, $a_1 = 1.312\,241$, $a_2 = -0.417\,699$ and $a_3 = 0$ so that the required least-squares approximation is given by

$$\sin x \approx -0.050\,469 + 1.312\,241x - 0.417\,699x^2,$$

which gives, for example, the values

$$\sin\left(\frac{\pi}{2}\right) \approx 0.980\,163$$

and

$$\sin\left(\frac{\pi}{4}\right) \approx 0.722\,505.$$

One drawback of the approach so far described is that the system of linear equations derived for either the continuous or the discrete least-squares problem tends to be ill conditioned, especially for a high-degree approximating polynomial. In such a situation, there is a large number of equations and the matrix has no sparseness which can be exploited to simplify the solution process. However, if we can find an alternative representation for our approximation polynomials in terms of some different basis for which the matrix is better conditioned and has some useful sparseness, then the whole problem may be significantly simplified. The way to achieve this is to use a system of **orthogonal polynomials**. For our brief discussion of this topic, we restrict attention to the continuous least-squares problem.

Suppose that $\phi_0, \phi_1, \ldots, \phi_M$ are polynomials of degree $0, 1, \ldots, M$, respectively. Our approximation p can be written in terms of these polynomials as

$$p(x) = a_0 \phi_0(x) + a_1 \phi_1(x) + \ldots + a_M \phi_M(x) \qquad (7.17)$$

and we wish to minimise

$$F(a_0, a_1, \ldots, a_M) = \int_a^b [f(x) - a_0 \phi_0(x) - a_1 \phi_1(x) - \ldots - a_M \phi_M(x)]^2 \, dx.$$

In the same way as before, we obtain the system of equations

$$\begin{pmatrix} c_{00} & c_{01} & c_{02} & \cdot & \cdot & c_{0M} \\ c_{10} & c_{11} & c_{12} & \cdot & \cdot & c_{1M} \\ c_{20} & c_{21} & c_{22} & \cdot & \cdot & c_{2M} \\ \cdot & \cdot & \cdot & \cdot & \cdot & \cdot \\ \cdot & \cdot & \cdot & \cdot & \cdot & \cdot \\ c_{M0} & c_{M1} & c_{M2} & \cdot & \cdot & c_{MM} \end{pmatrix} \begin{pmatrix} a_0 \\ a_1 \\ a_2 \\ \cdot \\ \cdot \\ a_M \end{pmatrix} = \begin{pmatrix} b_0 \\ b_1 \\ b_2 \\ \cdot \\ \cdot \\ b_M \end{pmatrix}, \quad (7.18)$$

where the coefficients of the system are given by

$$c_{ij} = c_{ji}$$

$$= \int_a^b \phi_i(x)\phi_j(x)\,dx.$$

It follows that, if we can find a system of polynomials $\phi_0, \phi_1, \ldots \phi_M$ such that ϕ_i is of degree i and such that

$$c_{ij} = \int_a^b \phi_i(x)\phi_j(x)\,dx$$

$$= 0 \qquad \text{whenever } i \neq j, \qquad (7.19)$$

then the resulting system of linear equations (7.18) will be diagonal, that is of the form

$$\begin{pmatrix} c_{00} & 0 & 0 & \cdot & \cdot & 0 \\ 0 & c_{11} & 0 & \cdot & \cdot & 0 \\ 0 & 0 & c_{22} & \cdot & \cdot & 0 \\ \cdot & \cdot & \cdot & \cdot & \cdot & \cdot \\ \cdot & \cdot & \cdot & \cdot & \cdot & \cdot \\ 0 & 0 & 0 & \cdot & \cdot & c_{MM} \end{pmatrix} \begin{pmatrix} a_0 \\ a_1 \\ a_2 \\ \cdot \\ \cdot \\ a_M \end{pmatrix} = \begin{pmatrix} b_0 \\ b_1 \\ b_2 \\ \cdot \\ \cdot \\ b_M \end{pmatrix},$$

which has the solution

$$a_j = b_j/c_{jj}$$

$$= \int_a^b f(x)\phi_j(x)\,dx \bigg/ \int_a^b [\phi_j(x)]^2\,dx. \qquad (7.20)$$

Such a system of polynomials are known as **orthogonal**. The members of any such system will depend on the interval over which we are seeking the approximation.

Example 7.5.2

On the interval $[0, \pi]$ the first few members of the system of orthogonal polynomials are obtained as follows.

Note that the polynomials are not uniquely determined by the orthogonality condition and we shall *normalise* the system by taking the leading coefficient of each one to be unity. Thus we seek polynomials of the form

$$\phi_j(x) = x^j + \alpha_{j-1} x^{j-1} + \ldots + \alpha_1 x + \alpha_0.$$

Note that, if these polynomials are to form an orthogonal system, then each ϕ_j is orthogonal to $\phi_0, \phi_1, \ldots, \phi_{j-1}$ from which it follows that ϕ_j must be orthogonal to the monomials $1, x, x^2, \ldots, x^{j-1}$ so that we must find $\alpha_0, \alpha_1, \ldots, \alpha_{j-1}$ such that

$$\int_0^\pi x^i \phi_j(x)\, dx = \int_0^\pi (x^{i+j} + \alpha_{j-1} x^{i+j-1} + \ldots + \alpha_1 x^{i+1} + \alpha_0 x^i)\, dx = 0$$

for $i = 0, 1, \ldots, j-1$. Since the leading coefficient of ϕ_0 is unity, it follows that

$$\phi_0(x) = 1$$

and then $\phi_1(x) = x + \alpha_0$ must satisfy

$$\int_0^\pi (x + \alpha_0)\, dx = \frac{\pi^2}{2} + \alpha_0 \pi$$

$$= 0$$

from which we deduce that $\alpha_0 = -\pi/2$ and so

$$\phi_1(x) = x - \frac{\pi}{2}.$$

Next $\phi_2(x) = x^2 + \alpha_1 x + \alpha_0$ must satisfy

$$\int_0^\pi (x^2 + \alpha_1 x + \alpha_0)\, dx = \frac{\pi^3}{3} + \frac{\alpha_1 \pi^2}{2} + \alpha_0 \pi$$

$$= 0$$

and

$$\int_0^\pi (x^3 + \alpha_1 x^2 + \alpha_0 x)\, dx = \frac{\pi^4}{4} + \frac{\alpha_1 \pi^3}{3} + \frac{\alpha_0 \pi^2}{2}$$

$$= 0$$

187

from which we obtain $\alpha_1 = -\pi$ and $\alpha_0 = \pi^2/6$ so that

$$\phi_2(x) = x^2 - \pi x + \frac{\pi^2}{6}.$$

We can use these functions in equations (7.19) and (7.20) to obtain the coefficients of the least squares quadratic approximation to $\sin x$ on $[0, \pi]$. We have

$$c_{jj} = \int_0^\pi [\phi_j(x)]^2 \, dx$$

and

$$b_j \int_0^\pi \phi_j(x) \sin x \, dx.$$

Hence $c_{00} = \pi$, $c_{11} = \pi^3/12$, $c_{22} = \pi^5/180$, $b_0 = 2$, $b_1 = 0$ and $b_2 = \pi^2/3 - 4$. We thus obtain the coefficients $a_0 = 0.636\,620$, $a_1 = 0$ and $a_2 = -0.417\,698$. Rearranging $p = a_0\phi_0 + a_1\phi_1 + a_2\phi_2$, we get

$$p(x) = -0.417\,698x^2 + 1.312\,236x - 0.050\,465,$$

which is very similar to the function obtained in Example 7.5.1.

The process can clearly be continued to find $\phi_3, \phi_4, \ldots$ and therefore higher-order approximations. There are alternative ways of generating orthogonal polynomials using the result which establishes that any such system satisfies a three-term recurrence relation.

This section serves only to give a brief introduction to an important area of numerical analysis and to demonstrate the benefits of using some mathematics before starting the actual solution process. We see here that a potentially very poorly conditioned and difficult problem has been recast using the idea of orthogonality into the simplest of linear-algebra problems—a diagonal system of equations. There are computational benefits to be gained in this way, too. Continuing as above, we would gradually build up an expansion of the original function in terms of our orthogonal basis polynomials. Such an expansion will usually be much more rapidly convergent than a more primitive power series expansion—and will usually provide numerical results of greater precision for less computational effort.

It should be pointed out that there is nothing special about the use of polynomials here as our approximating functions. There are many situations where it is more sensible to consider expansions of a function in terms of other basis functions. One important example of this is the use of the functions $\sin(kx)$ and $\cos(kx)$ which are orthogonal over $[-\pi, \pi]$ from which we can obtain the **Fourier series** expansion of a function. Such a representation of a function is of particular value when seeking to describe phenomena such as electromagnetic waves which have periodic behaviour.

EXERCISES 7.5

1 Derive the expressions

$$c_k = \sum_{i=0}^{N} x_i^k$$

and

$$b_k = \sum_{i=0}^{N} x_i^k f(x_i)$$

for the coefficients of the normal equations for the discrete least-squares approximation problem.

2 Show that the solution of the discrete least-squares problem for $M = N$ is the interpolation polynomial of degree at most N agreeing with f at the points $x_0, x_1, \ldots, x_N$.

3 Find the least-squares quartic approximations to $|x|$ on $[-1, 1]$ using
(a) the discrete metric with data points at 0, $\pm \frac{1}{3}$, $\pm \frac{2}{3}$ and ± 1 and
(b) the continuous L_2 metric.

4 Find the orthogonal polynomials of degree up to 4 (normalised to have unit leading coefficients) on $[-1, 1]$. Hence obtain the least-squares quartic approximation to $|x|$.

REFERENCES AND FURTHER READING

Barlow, J. L., and Bareiss, E. H. (1985), On roundoff error distributions in floating-point and logarithmic arithmetic, *Computing*, **34**, 325–347.

Chapra, S. C., and Canale, R. P. (1985), *Numerical Methods for Engineers*, McGraw-Hill, New York.

Cheney, E. W., and Kincaid, D. (1985), *Numerical Mathematics and Computing*, 2nd edition, Brooks–Cole, Monterey, California.

Clenshaw, C. W., and Curtis, A. R. (1960), A method for numerical integration on an automatic computer, *Numer. Math.*, **2**, 197–205.

Clenshaw, C. W., and Olver, F. W. J. (1984), Beyond floating-point, *J. Assoc. Comput. Mach.*, **31**, 319–328.

Davis, P. J., and Rabinowitz, P. (1984), *Methods of Numerical Integration*, 2nd edition, Academic Press, New York.

Feldstein, A., and Goodman, R. (1982), Loss of significance in floating-point subtraction and addition, *IEEE Trans. Comput.*, **C-31**, 328–335.

Feldstein, A., and Turner, P. R. (1986), Overflow, underflow and severe loss of precision in floating-point addition and subtraction, *IMA J. Numer. Anal.*, **6**, 241–251.

Forsyth, G. E., Malcolm, M. A., and Moler, C. B. (1977), *Computer Methods for Mathematical Computations*, Prentice-Hall, Englewood Cliffs, New Jersey.

Froberg, C.-K., (1975), Numerical Mathematics, Benjamin–Cummings, Menlo Park, California.

Goodman, R., and Feldstein, A. (1975), Roundoff error in products, *Computing*, **15**, 263–273.

Hamming, R. W., (1970), On the distribution of numbers, *Bell Syst. Tech. J.*, **49**, 1609–1625.

Hawkins, F. M., (1988), *Guide to analysis*, Macmillan, London.

Johnson, L. W., and Riess, R. D. (1982), *Numerical Analysis*. 2nd edition, Addison-Wesley, Reading, Massachusetts.

Kahan, W., and Palmer, J. (1979), On a proposed floating-point standard, SIGNUM *Newslett.*, October, 13–21.

Knuth, D. E., (1969), *The Art of Computer Programming*, Vol. 2, *Seminumerical Algorithms*, Addison-Wesley, Reading, Massachusetts.

Matsui, S., and Iri, M. (1981), An overflow/underflow-free floating-point representation of numbers, *J. Inform. Process.*, **4**, 123–133.

Morton, J. B., (1977), *Introduction to BASIC*, Pitman, London.

Olver, F. W. J., (1978), A new approach to error arithmetic, *SIAM J. Numer. Anal.*, **15**, 369–393.

Phillips, G. M., and Taylor, P. J. (1973), *Theory and Applications of Numerical Analysis*, Academic Press, London.

Schelin, C. W., (1983), Calculator function approximation, *Am. Math. Mon.*, **90**, 317–325.

Towers, D. A., (1988), *Guide to Linear Algebra*, Macmillan, London.

Turner, P. R., (1982), The distribution of leading significant digits, *IMA J. Numer. Anal.*, **2**, 407–412.

—(1984), Further revelations on l.s.d., *IMA J. Numer. Anal.*, **4**, 225–231.

Volder, J., (1959), The CORDIC computing technique, *IRE Trans. Comput.*, **EC8**, 330–334.

Walther, J., (1971) A unified algorithm for elementary functions, *AFIPS Conf. Proc.*, **38**, 379–385.

Waser, S., and Flynn, M. J. (1982), *Introduction to Arithmetic for Digital Systems Designers*, Holt, Rinehart and Winston, New York.

Wilkinson, J. H., (1963), Rounding Errors in Algebraic Processes, *Notes on Applied Science*, HMSO, London.

Yakowitz, S., and Szidarovszky, F. (1986), *An Introduction to Numerical Computations*, Macmillan, New York.

ANSWERS AND SOLUTIONS TO SELECTED EXERCISES

1 NUMBER REPRESENTATIONS AND ERRORS

EXERCISES 1.5

1 With chopping,

(a) $e \approx 0.2718 \times 10^1$,
(b) $e \approx 0.1010110111 \times 2^2$,
(c) $e \approx 0.2B7 \times 16^1$

With rounding,

(b) 0.1010111000×2^2,
(c) $0.2B8 \times 16^1$.

5 Truncation error is bounded by $|x|^7 [8/(8 - |x|)]/7!$. Since, for small x, $8 - x \approx 8$ we require $|x|^7 < 7! \times 10^{-10}$, that is, $|x| < 0.125\,99$.

6 For L_∞ norm, $|\exp x - 1 - x| = \exp x - 1 - x$ which has its maximum value on $[0, 1]$ at $x = 1$. So $\| \exp x - 1 - x \|_\infty = e - 2 = 0.718\,282$. $\| \exp x - x - 1 \|_1 = 0.218\,282$ and $\| \exp x - x - 1 \|_2 = 1.676\,18$.

2 ITERATIVE SOLUTION OF EQUATIONS; CONVERGENCE OF SEQUENCES

EXERCISES 2.2

1 $f(x) = 3x^3 - 5x^2 - 4x + 4$ is continuous, $f(0) = 4$ and $f(1) = -2$; so, by the intermediate-value theorem there is a root of $f(x) = 0$ in $[0, 1]$. Each iteration of bisection reduces the interval length by one half and so after 20 iterations the length is less than 2^{-20} which is less than 10^{-6}.

2 $f^{(3)}$ is positive everywhere and so there are at most three solutions. Also $f(-1)<0$, $f(0)>0$, $f(1)<0$ and $f(9)>0$ and so there are three sign changes.

EXERCISES 2.3

2 $x=\exp(x/2)/10 \Rightarrow 10x=\exp(x/2) \Rightarrow 100x^2=[\exp(x/2)]^2=\exp x$. Similarly, the other two are rearrangements as well.

(a) $g(x)>0$ for all values of x and so can only converge to a positive solution; $g'(x)=\exp(x/2)/20>1$ if $x>6$ and so will not converge to large root. It will converge to the solution in $[0,1]$; this is 0.10541 to five decimal places.

(b) This converges to the root near 9 which is 8.99951 to five decimal places.

(c) This converges to the negative solution, -0.09534 to five decimal places.

EXERCISES 2.4

1 For x between the two small solutions, $f(x)>0$ and so $x_1>x_0$ if and only if $f'(x_0)>0$; also $f'(x)=\exp x - 200x$ so that $f'(x)<0$ if x lies between the two zeros of f', the smaller of which is close to $x=1/200$. For $x_0 \leqslant 0.0049$, we get convergence to the negative solution. For x_0 very close to 0.005 the initial correction is large and so convergence to the large positive solution, near 9, results. For any $x_0 \in [0.0058, 7.28]$, Newton's method converges to the solution near 0.1.

3 $f(x)=1/x-c \to f'(x)=-1/x^2$ and so $x_{n+1}=x_n+x_n^2(1/x_n-c)=x_n(2-cx_n)$. The iteration function is therefore $g(x)=x(2-cx)$ and so $g'(x)=2(1-cx)$ from which it follows that $|g'(x)|<1$ for $x \in (1/2c, 3/2c)$.

EXERCISES 2.5

1 (a) $N_1 \geqslant 43$ and
  (b) $N_2 \geqslant 87$.

3 (b) Given any $h>0$, we must find N such that $|a_n+b_n-(a+b)|<h$ whenever $n>N$. We are given that $a_n \to a$ and $b_n \to b$ and so, for any $h_1>0$, there exist N_1, N_2 such that $|a_n-a|<h_1$ whenever $n>N_1$ and $|b_n-b|<h_1$ whenever $n>N_2$. Choose $h_1=h/2$ and then, if $n>N=\max(N_1,N_2)$, we have

$$|a_n + b_n - (a + b)| \leqslant |a_n - a| + |b_n - b|$$

$$< \frac{h}{2} + \frac{h}{2}$$

$$= h.$$

(c) Given $h > 0$ there exists N such that $|a_n| < h$ whenever $n > N$ and, since the sequence b_n is bounded, there exists M such that $|b_n| \leqslant M$ for all n. Therefore, if $n > N$,

$$|a_n b_n| = |a_n| |b_n| < Mh,$$

and so the result follows from Lemma 2.5.1.

4 Since the sequence a_n is increasing, $a_1 \leqslant a_n$ for all n and similarly $b_n \leqslant b_1$ for all n. Hence $a_1 \leqslant a_n \leqslant b_n \leqslant b_1$ and so the increasing sequence a_n is bounded above by b_1 while the decreasing sequence b_n is bounded below by a_1. Therefore, both sequences are bounded and monotone and so convergent. Suppose that $a_n \to a$, $b_n \to b$ and that $b < a$. Let $h = (a - b)/2$ so that $b + h = a - h$. There exist N_1, N_2 such that $|a_n - a| < h$ whenever $n > N_1$ and $|b_n - b| < h$ whenever $n > N_2$. Therefore, if $n > N = \max(N_1, N_2)$, it follows that $a - h < a_n < a + h$ and $b - h < b_n < b + h$ and so, in particular, $b_n < b + h = a - h < a_n$ which contradicts the fact that $a_n \leqslant b_n$ for all n.

5 Again for n sufficiently large we have $a - h < a_n < a + h$ and $a - h < b_n < a + h$ and so $a - h < a_n \leqslant c_n \leqslant b_n < a + h$ which implies that $c_n \to a$ as required.

EXERCISES 2.6

2

$$x_{n+1} - \frac{1}{c} = -cx_n^2 + 2x_n - \frac{1}{c}$$

$$= -c\left(x_n^2 - \frac{2x_n}{c} + \frac{1}{c^2} \right)$$

$$= -c\left(x_n - \frac{1}{c} \right)^2.$$

Hence $x_{n+1} - 1/c < 0$. Also, if $x_n < 1/c$, then $x_{n+1} = x_n(2 - cx_n) > x_n(2 - 1) = x_n$ as required. Hence x_n is convergent; denote its limit by a. Then $x_{n+1} - 1/c \to a - 1/c$ and $-c(x_n - 1/c)^2 \to -c(a - 1/c)^2$. From the first part it now follows that $a = 1/c$.

It follows for the special case of normalised binary floating-point numbers that

$$x_n - \frac{1}{c} = -c^{2^{n-1}} \left(x_0 - \frac{1}{c} \right)^{2^n}$$

and since $c < 2$ and $x_0 - 1/c \leqslant \frac{1}{4}$, it follows that after five iterations the error is less than $2^{31}/4^{32} = 2^{-33}$.

4 By the mean-value theorem, we have $x_{n+1} - s = (x_n - s)g'(\theta_n)$ and, since $-1 < g'(\theta_n) < 0$, it follows that $x_{n+1} - s > 0$ if and only if $x_n - s < 0$. Also $|x_{n+1} - s| < |x_n - s|$ and so the result follows.

3 SERIES APPROXIMATION OF FUNCTIONS; CONVERGENCE OF SERIES

EXERCISES 3.2

1 (a)
$$\frac{1}{r(r+2)} = \frac{1/r - 1/(r+2)}{2}$$

and so
$$2s_n = \left(1 - \frac{1}{3}\right) + \left(\frac{1}{2} - \frac{1}{4}\right) + \left(\frac{1}{3} - \frac{1}{5}\right) + \ldots + \left(\frac{1}{n} - \frac{1}{n+2}\right);$$

then $s_n = \frac{3}{4} - 1/2(n+1) - 1/2(n+2) \to \frac{3}{4}$ as $n \to \infty$.

(b) 1,
(c) $-\frac{1}{4}$,
(d) $\frac{5}{4}$,
(e) $-\frac{3}{4}$.

EXERCISES 3.3

1 (a) Convergent by comparison with $\sum 1/r(r+1)$, or by Exercises 3.2, 1(a) above.
(b), (c) Divergent by comparison with $\sum 1/r$.
(d) Convergent by the ratio test or by comparison with $\sum 1/2^r$.
(e) Convergent by the ratio test.
(f) Divergent by comparison with $\sum 1/r$.
(g) Convergent by the ratio test.

2 Firstly, $s_n \to s$, say, and so $s_{2n} \to s$ also. Hence $s_{2n} - s_n \to s - s = 0$. However,
$$s_{2n} - s_n = a_{n+1} + a_{n+2} + \ldots + a_{2n}$$
$$\geqslant na_{2n},$$

since there are n terms each of which is greater than or equal to a_{2n} because the sequence a_n is decreasing. Therefore $na_{2n} \to 0$ and so $2na_{2n} \to 0$. Also

$$(2n+1)a_{2n+1} = 2na_{2n+1} + a_{2n+1}$$
$$\leqslant 2na_{2n} + a_{2n+1}$$
$$\rightarrow 0$$

since $a_{2n+1} \leqslant a_{2n}$ and $a_n \rightarrow 0$. The result follows.

EXERCISES 3.4

2 The decreasing condition in Exercises 3.3, **2**, is needed since, for example, $\sum(-1)^r/r$ is convergent but $na_n = (-1)^n \nrightarrow 0$.

3 Suppose that $|b_n| \leqslant M$ for all n. Then $|a_n b_n| \leqslant M|a_n|$ and, since $\sum|a_n|$ is convergent, it follows, by the comparison test, that $\sum|a_n b_n|$ is too.

EXERCISES 3.5

1 (a) $R = 2$,
(b) $R = \infty$,
(c) $R = 1$.

2 Suppose that $\sum a_n x^n$ has a radius of convergence R. Then $|a_{n+1}/a_n| \rightarrow 1/R$ from which it follows that $|(n+1)a_{n+1}/na_n| \rightarrow 1/R$, also. Thus $\sum na_n x^{n-1}$ has a radius of convergence $1/(1/R) = R$, as required.

3
$$\ln(1-x) = -x - \frac{x^2}{2} - \frac{x^3}{3} - \dots.$$

With $x = \frac{1}{3}$ the tail of the series is

$$\frac{-1}{N \times 3^N} - \frac{1}{(N+1) \times 3^{N+1}} - \frac{1}{(N+2) \times 3^{N+2}} - \dots.$$

This truncation error is bounded by $(1 + \frac{1}{3} + \frac{1}{9} + \dots)/(N \times 3^N) = 1/(2N \times 3^{N-1})$ which is less than 5×10^{-7} for $N \geqslant 12$ so that we require the first 11 terms.

EXERCISES 3.6

1
$$y = \sum c_r x^r,$$
$$y'' = \sum r(r-1)c_r x^{r-2}$$

and so we get

$$y'' + x^2 y = \sum r(r-1)c_r x^{r-2} + \sum c_r x^{r+2}$$
$$= 0$$

and comparing coefficients of 1 and of x we get $2c_2 = 0$ and $6c_3 = 0$. For $n > 1$ the coefficient of x^n is $(n+2)(n+1)c_{n+2} + c_{n-2}$ and so $c_{n+2} = -c_{n-2}/(n+2)(n+1)$. Hence $c_6 = c_{10} = c_{14} = \ldots = 0$ and $c_7 = c_{11} = \ldots = 0$ so that

$$y = c_0 + c_4 x^4 + c_8 x^8 + \ldots + x(c_1 + c_5 x^4 + c_9 x^8 + \ldots)$$

$$= c_0 u(x) + c_1 x v(x).$$

Both series are convergent for all values of x.

4 INTERPOLATION AND APPROXIMATE EVALUATION OF FUNCTIONS

EXERCISES 4.2

1 Subtracting row k from row j yields a row of the determinant in which each element has the factor $x_j - x_k$. Hence the determinant is zero if any two interpolation points are equal. (To prove the converse implication, suppose that the determinant is zero. Then there is a linear combination of the columns which is identically zero. This represents a polynomial of degree N which vanishes at all the points $x_0, x_1, \ldots, x_N$, but such a polynomial has at most N distinct zeros and so two of these points must be equal.)

2 Both values are 0.9902 to four decimal places.

4 The error is bounded by $(x - x_0)(x - x_1)(x - x_2)(x - x_3)/24$ since $|f^{(4)}(x)| \leqslant 1$ for all x. Here x lies between x_1 and x_2 and, writing $x = x_0 + sh$ where $h = 0.1$, we have

$$(x - x_0)(x - x_1)(x - x_2)(x - x_3) = s(s-1)(s-2)(s-3) \times 10^{-4}.$$

This function has turning points at $s = 0.382, 1.5$ and 2.618 and so has a maximum absolute value on $[1,2]$ of $1.5^2 \times 0.5^2 = 0.5625$ so that the maximum possible error is about 2.3×10^{-6} which is less than 5×10^{-6} as desired.

EXERCISES 4.3

1 Using the points in the order $0.2, 0.3, 0.4, 0.0, 0.6$ the successive estimates are

$6.232,$

$6.232 + 0.04 \times 1.030 = 6.2732,$

$6.2732 + 0.04 \times 0.06 \times 0.15 = 6.2736,$

$$6.2736 + (0.04)(-0.06)(-0.16)(-0.165) = 6.2735,$$

$$6.2736 + (0.04)(-0.06)(-0.16)(0.24)(0.395) = 6.2735,$$

and so to three decimal places we have $f(0.24) \approx 6.274$.

3 For $k = 0$, we simply have $f[x_r] = f(x_r) = \Delta^0 f(x_r)/h^0 0!$. Suppose that the result holds for $k = n$, say, and consider $f[x_r, x_{r+1}, \ldots, x_{r+n}, x_{r+n+1}]$. By definition,

$$f[x_r, x_{r+1}, \ldots, x_{r+n}, x_{r+n+1}]$$

$$= \frac{f[x_{r+1}, \ldots, x_{r+n}, x_{r+n+1}] - f[x_r, x_{r+1}, \ldots, x_{r+n})}{(n+1)h}$$

$$= \frac{\Delta^n f(x_{r+1})/h^n n! - \Delta^n f(x_r)/h^n n!}{(n+1)h}$$

$$= \frac{\Delta^n f(x_{r+1}) - \Delta^n f(x_r)}{h^{n+1}(n+1)!}$$

$$= \frac{\Delta^{n+1} f(x_r)}{h^{n+1}(n+1)!}$$

as required.

EXERCISES 4.4

1 (a) Not a spline.
   (b) Spline of degree 1.
   (c) Spline of degree 2.
   (d) Not a spline.
   (e) Spline of degree 3.

2 $c_1 = -0.069\,78$ $\qquad$ $c_2 = -0.008\,50$ $\qquad$ $c_3 = -0.014\,03$.

Then

$d_0 = -0.023\,26$ $\quad$ $d_1 = 0.020\,43$ $\quad$ $d_2 = -0.001\,84$ $\quad$ $d_3 = 0.004\,68$,

$b_0 = 0.716\,36$ $\quad$ $b_1 = 0.454\,85$ $\quad$ $b_2 = 0.298\,04$ $\quad$ $b_3 = 0.232\,45$.

Thus

$$\ln(2.5) \approx 0.6931 + 0.5 \times 0.454\,85 - 0.5^2 \times 0.069\,78 + 0.5^3 \times 0.020\,43$$

$$\approx 0.9056.$$

EXERCISES 4.5

1
$$\sigma_{k+1} + \sigma_{k+2} + \ldots + \sigma_n = \sigma_k\left(\frac{1}{2} + \frac{1}{4} + \ldots + \frac{1}{2^{n-k}}\right)$$

$$= \sigma_k\left(1 - \frac{1}{2^{n-k}}\right)$$

$$= \sigma_k - \sigma_n.$$

Since $1.23 \in (1,2)$ and the error in multiplication is bounded by $x_0/2^n$, we require $n = 8$ to achieve the required accuracy. Take $x_0 = 1.23$ and $z_0 = 1.12$ with $y_0 = 0$ and $\delta_k = \text{sgn}(z_k)$ to get

$\delta_0 = +1 \qquad y_1 = 1.23 \qquad\qquad z_1 = 0.12,$

$\delta_1 = +1 \qquad y_2 = 1.23 + \dfrac{1.23}{2} \qquad z_2 = 0.12 - \tfrac{1}{2}$

$\qquad\qquad\qquad\; = 1.845 \qquad\qquad\quad = -0.38,$

$\delta_2 = -1 \qquad y_3 = 1.845 - \dfrac{1.23}{4} \qquad z_3 = -0.38 + 0.25$

$\qquad\qquad\qquad\; = 1.5375 \qquad\qquad\quad = -0.13,$

$\delta_3 = -1 \qquad y_4 = 1.383\,75 \qquad\qquad z_4 = -0.005,$

$\delta_4 = -1 \qquad y_5 = 1.306\,875 \qquad\quad z_5 = 0.0575,$

$\delta_5 = +1 \qquad y_6 = 1.345\,312\,5 \qquad z_6 = 0.026\,25,$

and so on until we obtain $y_9 = 1.378\,945$ which indeed has an error of less than 2^{-7}.

5 NUMERICAL CALCULUS

EXERCISES 5.2

1 The weights at the points $-1, 0, 1, 2$ are $\frac{8}{3}, -\frac{4}{3}, \frac{8}{3}, 0$, respectively. The degree of precision is 3.

2 The final Simpson's rule estimate is $0.693\,147\,6$ which is in error by 5×10^{-7}. The step length used here is $\frac{1}{16}$ and $f^{(4)}(x) = 24/x^5$ so that $|f^{(4)}(x)| \leqslant 24$ on $[1,2]$. Hence the error in the composite Simpson rule is bounded by $24 \times 16^{-4}/180$ which is approximately 2×10^{-6} so that the predicted accuracy has been achieved.

4 (a) $f''(x) = (x^2 - 1)\exp(-x^2/2)/\sqrt{2\pi}$ and $x^2 - 1 \leqslant 3$ on $[0,2]$ while $\exp(-x^2/2) \leqslant 1$ so that $f''(x) < 1.2$ throughout the interval of interest. We thus require that $2h^2 \times 1.2/12 < 10^{-7}$ or $h^2 < 5 \times 10^{-7}$ which implies that $h < 7.07 \times 10^{-4}$. In this case, $h = 2/N$ and a total of $N + 1$ points are needed. We get $N \geqslant 2829$ and so 2830 points in all.

(b) With Simpson's rule, we find that $|f^{(4)}(x)| < 5/\sqrt{2\pi} < 2$ and so require that $h^4 < 4.5 \times 10^{-6}$ and hence $h < 0.046$ will suffice. Thus, 45 points are needed.

7 The ratio is approximately $\frac{1}{16}$.

EXERCISES 5.3

1 The nodes are at $\pm[(3 \pm 4\sqrt{3/10})/7]^{1/2}$ with weights $(6 \pm \sqrt{10/3})/12$.

EXERCISES 5.4

2 $\quad f(x_0 \pm h) = f_0 \pm hf'_0 + \dfrac{h^2 f''_0}{2} \pm \dfrac{h^3 f_0^{(3)}}{6} + \dfrac{h^4 f_0^{(4)}}{24} \pm \dfrac{h^5 f_0^{(5)}}{120} + \dfrac{h^6 f^{(6)}(\theta_\pm)}{720}.$

Denote $f(x_0 + kh)$ by f_k. Then

$$f_1 - 2f_0 + f_{-1} = h^2 f''_0 + \frac{h^4 f_0^{(4)}}{12} + \frac{h^6 f^{(6)}(\theta_1)}{360}$$

and

$$f_2 - 2f_0 + f_{-2} = 4h^2 f''_0 + \frac{4h^4 f_0^{(4)}}{3} + \frac{8h^6 f^{(6)}(\theta_2)}{45}.$$

Subtracting the second equation from 16 times the first gives the required result and shows that the truncation error is of the order of h^4.

3 Subtracting fifth-order Taylor expansions for $f(x_0 \pm h)$ and for $f(x_0 \pm 2h)$ and eliminating the first-derivative terms yields the formula

$$f^{(3)}(x_0) \approx \frac{f_2 - 2f_1 + 2f_{-1} - f_{-2}}{2h^3}.$$

4 The following results should be compared with the true value 7.389 06.

	Estimates of $f'(x_0)$			Estimates of $f''(x_0)$	
h	(5.23)	(5.25)	(5.26)	(5.27)	(5.28)
1	12.696 48	8.683 63	7.111 66	8.025 71	7.299 27
0.1	7.771 14	7.401 38	7.389 03	7.395 21	7.389 04
0.01	7.426 12	7.389 17	7.389 05	7.389 12	7.389 05
0.001	7.392 75	7.389 05	7.389 05	7.388 00	7.387 50

Note how the second-derivative approximations are deteriorating for $h = 0.001$ because of rounding error.

EXERCISES 5.5

1 Without derivatives the bracket is $[0.8, 3.2]$, and with derivatives it is $[1.6, 3.2]$.

2 The midpoint of the initial bracket is 2.4 and $f(2.4) > f(1.6)$ so that the initial bracket is shifted left to $[0.8, 2.4]$. The minimum of the quadratic is at 1.8909 which is taken as the midpoint of the next interval. After two more iterations, we have $x^* = 1.989\,05$ with an error of less than 0.1. (The actual error is much less than this tolerance as the minimum we seek is at $x = 2$.)

6 DIFFERENTIAL EQUATIONS

EXERICSES 6.2

1 The estimated value of $y(1)$ with $h = 0.05$ is 2.705 823 which has an error of about 0.0124 compared with the error of about 0.0451 in Example 6.2.1.

2 For $h = 0.01$, we get the following answers (the answers to Exercises 6.2, **3**, and Exercises 6.3, **4**, are also shown).

x	The corrected euler method	Heun's method	The Runge–Kutta formula	Adams' predictor–corrector method
0.1	0.005 000 5	0.005 000 5	0.005 000 5	0.005 000 5
0.2	0.020 015 9	0.020 016 0	0.020 016 0	0.020 016 0
0.3	0.045 121 7	0.045 121 8	0.045 121 9	0.045 121 9
0.4	0.080 515 6	0.080 515 8	0.080 516 1	0.080 516 1
0.5	0.126 586 2	0.126 586 5	0.126 587 3	0.126 587 3
0.6	0.183 993 9	0.183 994 5	0.183 995 9	0.183 995 9
0.7	0.253 776 7	0.253 777 7	0.253 780 2	0.253 780 2
0.8	0.337 499 7	0.337 501 4	0.337 505 7	0.337 505 6
0.9	0.437 480 4	0.437 483 1	0.437 490 0	0.437 490 0
1.0	0.557 146 0	0.557 150 1	0.557 161 6	0.557 161 6

3 If f is a function of x alone then $k_1 = f(x_k)$, $k_2 = k_3 = f(x_{k+1/2})$ and $k_4 = f(x_{k+1})$. Hence

$$\int_{x_k}^{x_{k+1}} f(x)\,dx = y(x_{k+1}) - y(x_k)$$

$$\approx y_{k+1} - y_k$$

$$= \frac{h[f(x_k) + 4f(x_{k+1/2}) + f(x_{k+1})]}{6}$$

which is Simpson's rule for the interval $[x_k, x_{k+1}]$.

EXERCISES 6.3

1 The equations are

(a) $$\beta_0 + \beta_1 + \beta_2 + \beta_3 = 1,$$

(b) $$\beta_0 \qquad - \beta_2 - 2\beta_3 = \tfrac{1}{2},$$

(c) $$\beta_0 \qquad + \beta_2 + 4\beta_3 = \tfrac{1}{3},$$

(d) $$\beta_0 \qquad -\beta_2 - 8\beta_3 = \tfrac{1}{4}.$$

(b)–(d) gives $\beta_3 = \tfrac{1}{24}$ from which (b) and (c) imply that

$$\beta_0 - \beta_2 = \tfrac{7}{12}$$

and

$$\beta_0 + \beta_2 = \tfrac{1}{6}.$$

Hence $\beta_0 = \tfrac{9}{24}$, $\beta_2 = -\tfrac{5}{24}$ and then $\beta_1 = \tfrac{19}{24}$.

2 In estimating the local truncation error, we assume that $y(x_k) = y_k$ in which case the error in the Taylor series approximation (6.14) is $h^4 y^{(4)}(\theta_k)/24$. Similarly, from equation (5.25), the error in the approximation for y_k'' is of the form $h^2 y^{(4)}(\theta)/6$ and so for $h^2 y_k''/2$ the error is $h^4 y^{(4)}(\theta)/12$. For the third-derivative term, the error in estimating $h^3 y_k^{(3)}/6$ is of order h^5 and so the overall local truncation error is of order h^4.

3 With repeated use of the corrector formula, we get estimates of $y(1)$ using $h = 0.1$ and 0.05 to $2.721\,316$ and $2.718\,547$. (This example shows a tendency for the corrector formula to overcorrect.)

4 See answer to Exercises 6.2, **2**.

EXERCISES 6.5

1 The general solution is $y \approx K \exp(x^3)$; so $y(0) = K$ and $y(1) = Ke = ey(0)$. The boundary condition $y(0) + y(1) = 4$ is therefore equivalent to $(1 + e)y(0) = 4$ which is a linear equation for $y(0)$. In the absence of any numerical errors the secant method will solve any such equation exactly in just one iteration.

7 LINEAR EQUATIONS

EXERCISES 7.2

1 The following is a table of the results for $N = 2, 3, \ldots, 7$ by which stage we see the deterioration in precision which gets rapidly worse.

N	2	3	4	5	6	7
x_1	1.000 000	0.999 999	0.999 999	1.000 075	1.000 186	1.000 996
x_2	1.000 000	1.000 005	1.000 014	0.998 680	0.995 303	0.964 353
x_3		0.999 995	0.999 976	1.005 484	1.029 024	1.318 144
x_4			1.000 012	0.991 939	0.929 630	−0.167 926
x_5				1.003 863	1.073 416	3.047 379
x_6					0.972 382	−0.706 517
x_7						1.543 936

4 Suppose that the first two rows of a tridiagonal matrix are interchanged. The resulting matrix has a non-zero entry in the 1, 3 position where the original matrix has a zero. The insertion of any non-zero element above the tridiagonal array will necessarily persist throughout the elimination process and therefore complicates the back substitution.

EXERCISES 7.3

2 The initial solutions for $N = 2, 3, 4$ are identical with those obtained in Exercises 7.2, **1**, but for this ill-conditioned system the iterative refinement results in a slight *loss* of accuracy. The precision of the solution deteriorates more rapidly and more severely than for the straightforward Gauss elimination solution and the iterative refinement serves only to exacerbate the situation. For example, for $N = 8$, we get the initial solution

$$x_1 = 2.905,$$

$$x_2 = -27.41,$$

$$x_3 = 69.71,$$

$$x_4 = 42.45,$$

$$x_5 = 33.76,$$

$$x_6 = -948.1,$$

$$x_7 = 1499,$$

$$x_8 = -665.1$$

and the 'refined' solution

$$x_1 = 2.880,$$

$$x_2 = -27.24,$$

$$x_3 = 69.71,$$

$$x_4 = 42.45,$$

$$x_5 = 33.76,$$
$$x_6 = -956.2,$$
$$x_7 = 1515,$$
$$x_8 = -674.2$$

EXERCISES 7.4

1 The system of equations to be solved is

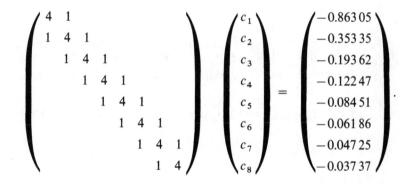

Working with a tolerance of 10^{-5} the Jacobi iteration converges in 13 iterations while the Gauss–Seidel iteration requires just six iterations. The solution obtained with the latter is

$$c_1 = -0.209\,07,$$
$$c_2 = -0.026\,75,$$
$$c_3 = -0.037\,28,$$
$$c_4 = -0.017\,75,$$
$$c_5 = -0.014\,18,$$
$$c_6 = -0.010\,06,$$
$$c_7 = -0.007\,43,$$
$$c_8 = -0.007\,49.$$

Thus, for example, in $[3, 4]$ the spline is

$$1.098\,61 + 0.605\,63(x - 3) - 0.026\,75(x - 3)^2 - 0.003\,51(x - 3)^3,$$

from which we obtain the approximation $\ln(3.5) \approx 1.394\,21$.

EXERCISES 7.5

2 If $M = N$, we seek the polynomial of degree at most N which minimises the discrete least-squares error at $N + 1$ points. The Lagrange interpolation polynomial results in exact agreement at these points and so the discrete least-squares measure of the error is zero which is clearly the minimum error attainable.

3 (a) For the given seven points we find that $c_0 = 7$, $c_1 = 0$, $c_2 = 3.1111$, $c_3 = 0$, $c_4 = 2.4198$, $c_5 = 0$, $c_6 = 2.1783$, $c_7 = 0$, $c_8 = 2.0783$ and $b_0 = 4$, $b_1 = 0$, $b_2 = 2.6667$, $b_3 = 0$, $b_4 = 2.2716$. Hence we obtain the coefficients of the quartic approximation

$$0.0870 + 1.7243x^2 - 0.8155x^4.$$

4 $\phi_0(x) = 1$, $\phi_1(x) = x$, $\phi_2(x) = x^2 - \frac{1}{3}$, $\phi_3(x) = x^3 - 3x/5$, $\phi_4(x) = x^4 - 6x^2/7 + \frac{3}{35}$. Hence, for $f(x) = |x|$, the coefficients b_j are $b_0 = 1$, $b_1 = 0$, $b_2 = \frac{1}{6}$, $b_3 = 0$, $b_4 = -0.009\,524$ while $c_{00} = 2$, $c_{22} = \frac{8}{45}$ and $c_{44} = 0.011\,61$ so that the (continuous) least-squares quartic approximation to $|x|$ on $[-1, 1]$ is

$$0.5 + 0.9375\phi_2(x) - 0.8203\phi_4(x) = 0.1172 + 1.6406x^2 - 0.8203x^4.$$

INDEX